21ST CENTURY

PUBLISHED BY
WISE PUBLICATIONS
8/9 FRITH STREET, LONDON, W1D 3JB, ENGLAND.

EXCLUSIVE DISTRIBUTORS:
MUSIC SALES LIMITED
DISTRIBUTION CENTRE, NEWMARKET ROAD,
BURY ST EDMUNDS, SUFFOLK, IP33 3YB, ENGLAND.
MUSIC SALES PTY LIMITED
120 ROTHSCHILD AVENUE, ROSEBERY, NSW 2018, AUSTRALIA.

ORDER NO. AM89700
ISBN 0-7119-3057-0
THIS BOOK © COPYRIGHT 2004 BY WISE PUBLICATIONS.

COMPILED BY NICK CRISPIN.
MUSIC ARRANGEMENTS BY JASON BROADBENT.
MUSIC PROCESSED BY PAUL EWERS MUSIC DESIGN.

COVER DESIGN BY FRESH LEMON.
PRINTED IN THE UNITED KINGDOM BY
CALIGRAVING LIMITED, THETFORD, NORFOLK.

YOUR GUARANTEE OF QUALITY:
AS PUBLISHERS, WE STRIVE TO PRODUCE EVERY
BOOK TO THE HIGHEST COMMERCIAL STANDARDS.
THE MUSIC HAS BEEN FRESHLY ENGRAVED AND
THE BOOK HAS BEEN CAREFULLY DESIGNED
TO MINIMISE AWKWARD PAGE TURNS AND TO
MAKE PLAYING FROM IT A REAL PLEASURE.
PARTICULAR CARE HAS BEEN GIVEN TO
SPECIFYING ACID-FREE, NEUTRAL-SIZED
PAPER MADE FROM PULPS WHICH HAVE
NOT BEEN ELEMENTAL CHLORINE BLEACHED.
THIS PULP IS FROM FARMED SUSTAINABLE
FORESTS AND WAS PRODUCED WITH
SPECIAL REGARD FOR THE ENVIRONMENT.
THROUGHOUT, THE PRINTING AND BINDING HAVE
BEEN PLANNED TO ENSURE A STURDY,
ATTRACTIVE PUBLICATION WHICH
SHOULD GIVE YEARS OF ENJOYMENT.
IF YOUR COPY FAILS TO MEET OUR HIGH STANDARDS,
PLEASE INFORM US AND WE WILL GLADLY REPLACE IT.

www.musicsales.com

WISE PUBLICATIONS
LONDON / NEW YORK / PARIS / SYDNEY / COPENHAGEN / BERLIN / MADRID / TOKYO

BEHIND BLUE EYES

WORDS & MUSIC BY PETE TOWNSHEND

E   G6   Dsus2   Cadd9   Asus2   A

G*   C   D   G   Esus4   Bm

Intro | E | G6 | Dsus2 | Dsus2 |

| Cadd9 | Cadd9 | Asus2 | Asus2 ‖

Verse 1

E   G6
No one knows what it's like

        Dsus2
To be the bad man,

        Cadd9
To be the sad man,

    A   G*   A
Be - hind blue eyes.

E   G6
And no one knows what it's like

        Dsus2
To be hated,

        Cadd9
To be fated,

        A   G*A
To telling on - ly lies.

<pre>
                  C   D   G
Chorus 1   But my dreams, they aren't as empty
                      C   D   E   Esus⁴ E
            As my conscience seems to be
                  Bm   C
            I have hours, only lonely
                      D
            My love is vengeance
                      Asus² │ Asus² │
            That's never free.

                  E   G⁶
Verse 2   No one knows what it's like
                      Dsus²
            To feel these feelings
                  Cadd⁹
            Like I do,
                      Asus²
            And I blame you!
            E   G⁶
            No one bites back as hard
                  Dsus²
            On their anger,
                      Cadd⁹
            None of my pain and woe
                  Asus²
            Can show through.

Chorus 2   As Chorus 1

                      E   G⁶   Dsus²
Bridge   Discover   L - I - M - P,   say it,
                  Cadd⁹   Asus²
            Discover   L - I - M - P,   say it,
                      E   G⁶   Dsus²
            Discover   L - I - M - P,   say it,
                  Cadd⁹   Asus²
            Discover   L - I - M - P,   say it,
</pre>

3

Verse 3	**E** **G6** No one knows what it's like

E   **G6**

Verse 3   No one knows what it's like

               Dsus2

To be mis - treated,

               Cadd9

To be de - feated,

           Asus2

Be - hind blue eyes.

        E   **G6**

And no one knows how to say

               Dsus2

That they're sorry,

               Cadd9

And don't worry,

           Asus2

I'm not telling lies.

Chorus 3   As Chorus 1

        E   **G6**

Outro   No one knows what it's like

               Dsus2

To be the bad man,

               Cadd9

To be the sad man,

       A   **G***   **A**

Be - hind blue eyes.

COMFORT IN SOUND

WORDS & MUSIC BY GRANT NICHOLAS

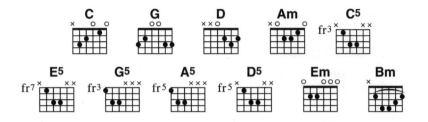

Intro | C G | D | C G | D ‖

Verse 1
    C   G   D   C
We fall right in and suffer the sins
       G   D   C
Try to pull things round when the air starts to thin
   G   D
We nurse re - grets
               Am
Restricted in our own belief
   C
A new disease

Verse 2
    C   G   D   C
We shake new hands, the victims of fate
       G   D   C
We tread new ground misfortune con - veys
   G   D
You tear your - self apart
           Am
Wishing to be born again,
   C
A different man.

Chorus 1

C5   E5   G5
  Com - fort in sound

  A5   C5
It's all a - round

    G5   D5
Ease back the strain

    A5   C5
Come heal your pain

    E5   G5
Com - fort in sound

   A5   C5
It's all a - round you now,

           C   G |D |C G |D ‖
Comfort in sound.

Verse 3

C   G   D   C
  We suffer love together as one

  G   D   C
An empty heart with nowhere to turn

  G   D
We find our - selves

               Am
Looking back an - other way

  C
A brand new day.

Chorus 2

C5   E5   G5
  Com - fort in sound

  A5   C5
It's all a - round

    G5   D5
Ease back the strain

    A5   C5
Come heal your pain

    E5   G5
Com - fort in sound

   A5   C5
It's all a - round you now, yeah.

Guitar solo | Em | D | A | A |

| Em | Bm | A | A ||

       C   G   D   C

Verse 4   So - lution gone, emotions a - blaze

      G   D   C

A life so strong just faded a - way

        G   D

You find your - self

                    Am

Searching for a quick release

   C

A new belief.

    C5   E5   G5

Chorus 3   Com - fort in sound

       A5   C5

It's all a - round

      G5   D5

Ease back the strain

      A5   C5

Come heal your pain

     E5   G5

Com - fort in sound

    A5   C5

It's all a - round you now

            C   G |D |C G |D |D |D ||

Comfort in sound.

COLOURS IN WAVES

WORDS & MUSIC BY JOEL CADBURY, JAMES McDONALD & BRETT SHAW

Chords: Em9   Em   Bm7   A6   D   A6/C#   G   A   E5   B5   A5

Intro

| Em9 | Em9 | Em9 | Em |

| Em9 | Em9 | Em9 | Em9 |

| Em9 | Em9 | Bm7 | A6 |

| Em9 | Em9 | Bm7 | A6 |

Verse 1

Em9
Each and every day

Bm7   A6
Colours in waves

Em9
Love and nights cause sparks

Bm7   A6
Tearing us a - part.

Pre-chorus 1

Em9
Street lights fading cuts my heart

          A6/C#
Knowing that the time is past

Em9
Comes in waves that don't belong

  D   A6/C#
To me they're silent.

Chorus 1

Em   G
Fall back on what you've done
D   A
I'll be the only one
        Em   G
These colours be - fore my eyes
D   A E_5
I'll be for - ever colour blind

Link 1

| E_5 | E_5 | B_5 | A_5 | |
| E_5 | E_5 | B_5 | A_5 | ‖ |

Verse 2   As Verse 1

Verse 3   As Verse 1

Link 2   As Link 1

Pre-chorus 2   As Pre-chorus 1

Chorus 3

Em   G
Fall back on what you've done
D   A
I'll be the only one
        Em   G
These colours be - fore my eyes
D   A Em_9 | Em_9 ‖
I'll be fo - rever colour blind.

Outro

         Bm_7 A_6 Em_9 | Em_9 | Bm_7 | A_6 ‖
These co - lours in waves.

DANCE COMMANDER

WORDS & MUSIC BY TYLER SPENCER, JOSEPH FREZZA, STEPHEN NAWARA, ANTHONY SELPH & COREY MARTIN

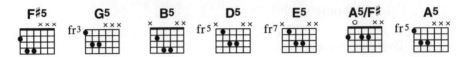

F#5   G5   B5   D5   E5   A5/F#   A5

Intro

    N.C.
You must have been a dance commander,

Giving out the order for fun

You must have been a dance commander,

You know that he's the only one who gives the orders here,

Alright, who gives the orders here, alright.

Chorus 1

          F#5   **G5**   **B5**
It would be awesome   if we could dance-a

          F#5   **G5**   **B5**
It would be awesome yeah,   let's take a chance-a

          F#5   **G5**   **B5**
It would be awesome yeah,   let's start the show,

          D5
Because you never know, you never know,

    E5
You never know until you go.

A5/F# **G5**   **B5**
       Al - right,

A5/F# **G5**   **B5**
       Al - right,

       A5/F#   **G5** **B5**
Who gives the orders here?

       A5/F#   **G5** **B5**
Who gives the orders here?

Verse 2

F♯5   G5
The lads are strong, the orders are in

        B5
The dance commander's ready to send

F♯5   G5
Radio message from HQ

B5
Dance commander we love you.

       F♯5   G5   B5
Let's get this party started right yo,

       F♯5   G5   B5
Let's get this party started right.

Verse 3

   F♯5   G5   B5
I went to the store to get more fire to start the war,

F♯5   G5
Everybody in this club is whack,

             B5
I feel like I'm headed straight for a heart attack,

F♯5   G5
Girls are pretty, girls are nice,

B5
Take your chances roll the dice,

F♯5   G5   B5
             Now, take your chances.

Chorus 2

             F♯5   G5   B5
It would be awesome   if we could dance-a

             F♯5   G5   B5
It would be awesome yeah,   let's take a chance-a

             F♯5   G5   B5
It would be awesome yeah,   let's start the show,

             D5
Because you never know, you never know,

       E5
You never know until you go.

Bridge

B5   G5
  I wanna make it last forever, I wanna make it last for - ever,

                         A5   F♯5   B5
I wanna make it last for - ever, I wanna make it last for - ever.

                                                                G5
I wanna make it last forever, I wanna make it last for - ever,

                         A5   F♯5   B5
I wanna make it last for - ever, I wanna make it last for - ever.

                                                                    G5
cont.   I wanna make it last forever, I wanna make it last for - ever,
                                      A5   **F♯5**   **B5**
            I wanna make it last for - ever, I wanna make it last for - ever.

                                                                    G5
            I wanna make it last forever, I wanna make it last for - ever,
                                      A5   **F♯5**
            I wanna make it last for - ever, ooh baby!

            A5/F♯ G5   **B5**
Outro   Al - right,
            A5/F♯ G5   **B5**
                     Al - right,
              A5/F♯   **G5**
            You must have been the dance comm - ander
              B5
            You must have been the dance commander
              A5/F♯   **G5**
            You must have been the dance comm - ander
              B5
            You must have been the dance commander, come on!
            A5/F♯ G5   **B5**
                       Come on, come on, come on, come on!

            | **F♯5 G5** | **B5**   ‖

DARTS OF PLEASURE

WORDS & MUSIC BY ALEXANDER KAPRANOS & NICHOLAS McCARTHY

| F#m | A6 | E5 | E | Em | C |
| Am | B | A#5 | G | A | A7 |

fr3

Intro

| F#m A6 | F#m E5 ‖

Verse 1

F#m   A6   F#m E5
You are the latest con - tender

F#m   A6   F#m E5
You are the one to re - member

F#m   A6   F#m E5
You are the villain who sends her

E
Light or dark, fantastic passion

F#m   A6   F#m   E5
  I know that you will sur - render

F#m   A6   F#m   E5
  I know that you will sur - render

E
I want this fantastic passion

Em
  We'll have fantastic passion.

Chorus 1

C   Em
You can feel my lips undress your eyes,

              Am   Em
Undress your eyes, undress your eyes.

C
Words of love and words so leisured

Em
Words are poisoned darts of pleasure

B   Em N.C. A#5
Die and so you die

Verse 2

F#m   A6   F#m E5
 You are the latest ad - venture

F#m   A6   F#m E5
 You're an e - motion a - venger

F#m   A6   F#m E5
  You are the devil that sells her

E
Light or dark, fantastic passion

F#m   A6   F#m E5
 I know that you will sur - render

F#m A6   F#m E5
I know that you will sur - render

E
I want this fantastic passion

Em
 We'll have fantastic passion.

Chorus 2

C   Em
You can feel my lips undress your eyes,

     Am   Em
Undress your eyes, undress your eyes

C   Em
Skin can feel my lips they tingle, tense anticipation

Am   Em
This one is an easy one, feel the word and melt upon it.

C
Words of love and words so leisured

Em
Words are poisoned darts of pleasure

B   Em N.C.
Die and so you die.

Bass link   ‖: G | E | G | E   :‖

Outro

G   E
Ich heisse Superfantastisch!

G   E
Ich trinke Schampus und Lachsfisch!

G   A   E | E |
Ich heisse Su - per - fan - tas - tisch!

G   E
Ich heisse Superfantastisch!

G   E
Ich trinke Schampus und Lachsfisch!

G   A   E | E |
Ich heisse Su - per - fan - tas - tisch!

G   E
Ich heisse Superfantastisch!

G   E
Ich trinke Schampus und Lachsfisch!

G   A^7 E
Ich heisse Su - per - fan - tas - tisch!

FEELING THIS

WORDS & MUSIC BY MARK HOPPUS, TOM DELONGE & TRAVIS BARKER

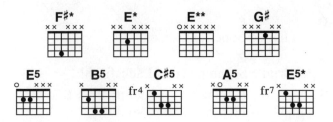

Riff | F#* E* E* E* E* E* | E* G#* E** ‖
Play Riff when indicated in song

Intro
> **Riff**   **Riff**
> Get ready for action!

Verse 1
> **Riff**
> I got no regret right now (I'm feeling this)
>
> **Riff**
> The air is so cold and low (I'm feeling this)
>
> **Riff**
> Let me go in her room (I'm feeling this)
>
> **Riff**
> I wanna take off her clothes (I'm feeling this)
>
> **Riff**
> Show me the way to bed (I'm feeling this)
>
> **Riff**
> Show me the way you move (I'm feeling this)
>
> **Riff**
> Fuck it, it's such a blur (I'm feeling this)
>
> **Riff**
> I love all the things you do. (I'm feeling this)

Chorus 1
> **E5**   **B5**   **C#5**
> Fate fell short this time
>
>   **A5**
> Your smile fades in the summer
>
> **E5**   **B5**   **C#5**
> Place your hand in mine
>
>   **A5**
> I'll leave when I wanna.

Link | **E*** | **F♯*** | **G♯** | **A*** ‖

Riff
Verse 2   Where do we go from here
                Riff
                Turn all the lights down now
                Riff
                Smiling from ear to ear (I'm feeling this)
                        Riff
                Our breathing has got too loud (I'm feeling this)
                Riff
                Show me the bedroom floor (I'm feeling this)
                Riff
                Show me the bathroom mirror (I'm feeling this)
                Riff
                We're taking this way too slow (I'm feeling this)
                Riff
                Take me away from here. (I'm feeling this)

Chorus 2   As Chorus 1

                N.C.
Chorus 3   As Chorus 1

                        E**
Middle   This place was never the same again

                After you came and went

                How can you say you meant anything different

                To anyone standing alone

                On the street with a cigarette

                On the first night we met
                E5
                Look to the past
                        B5
                And re - member and smile.
                        C♯5
                And maybe tonight
                        A5
                I can breathe for a while.

17

       E5*
I'm not in the scene

           B5
I think I'm fallin' asleep

           C#5
But then all that it means is

      A5   **N.C.**
I'll always be dreaming of you.

Chorus 4   As Chorus 1

Chorus 5   As Chorus 1

Chorus 6   As Chorus 1

E5   **B5**   **C#5**
Chorus 7   Fate   fell short   this   time
(Are we alone, do you feel it?)

           A5
Your smile   fades in the summer
  (So lost and disillusioned)

E5   **B5**   **C#5**
Place   your hand   in   mine
(Are we alone,   do you feel it?)

           A5
    I'll   leave when I wanna.
(So lost and disillusioned)

Chorus 8   As Chorus 7

FIRST IT GIVETH

WORDS & MUSIC BY JOSH HOMME & NICK OLIVERI

Chord diagrams: D*, Eb*, A*, F*, F**, D, Eb, A, F, F***, A**, D5, F5, Bb5, G5, Dm, Eb**, A***, F****, Eb5, A5, G5*, F#5/C#, C#5

⑥ = C ③ = Eb
⑤ = F ② = G
④ = Bb ① = C

Intro

| D* | Eb* | A* | F* |

| D* | Eb* | A* | F* ‖

| D* | Eb* | A* | F* |

| D* | Eb* | F* | F* ‖

Verse 1

D* Eb*   A*
  I'm in you

F*   D*
You're in me

Eb*   F** A*
I   can't tell

D* Eb*   A*
  You're so cruel

F*   D*
More than me

Eb*   A*
It is true

That's right.

Verse 2

D E♭   A
Loyal to

F   D
Only you

E♭   A
Up your sleeve

D E♭   F***
I want some (come on, take it)

　　A** F*** D
Of all   of   you (it's yours)

E♭   A
Trickin' me.

Chorus 1

D5　　　　　　　　　　　　　　　**F5   B♭5 G5**
First it giveth, then it taketh a - way_____

D5　　　　　　　　　　　　　　　**F5   B♭5 G5**
First it giveth, then it taketh a - way_____

D5　　　　　　　　　　　　　　　**F5   B♭5 G5**
First it giveth, then it taketh a - way_____

D5　　　　　　　　　　　　　　　**F5   B♭5 G5**
First it giveth, then it taketh a - way._____

Link 1

| **Dm**　　| **Dm E♭**** | **A*****　　| **A*** F******　　|

| **Dm**　　| **Dm E♭**** | **A*****　　| **A*** F******　　‖

Verse 3

D5 E♭5　　　**A5**
I   would beg

　　F5　　　**D5**
And I would plead

E♭5　　　**A5**
I   would shake

D*E♭* A*
　On a hook

F*　　　**D***
Dangling,

E♭*　　**A***
By the way

20

Verse 4

D E♭   A
I'm so young

    F   **D**
And beauti - ful

(That's right; I'm slick)
E♭   **F*** A****
I'm no fool.
D E♭   **F*****
  Time goes by

A   **D**
Tables turn
E♭   **A***
Now I know.

Chorus 2   As Chorus 1

Outro

D5   **G5*** **F♯5/C♯**   **B♭5 C♯5**
  First it   giveth, then it taketh a - way____
D5   **G5*** **F♯5/C♯**   **B♭5 C♯5**
  First it   giveth, then it taketh a - way.____
  B♭5 C♯5
A - way,
  B♭5 C♯5
A - way.

| **Dm** | **Dm E♭**** ‖

GOD PUT A SMILE UPON YOUR FACE

WORDS & MUSIC BY GUY BERRYMAN, CHRIS MARTIN, JON BUCKLAND & WILL CHAMPION

Db   E6   Eb7   Dmaj7   Amaj7   F#add9

Tune down one and a half tones

Intro
| Db | E6 | Eb7 | Eb7 Dmaj7 |

| Db | E6 | Eb7 | Dmaj7 |

Verse 1

Db   E6   Eb7   Dmaj7
Where do we go, nobody knows!

Db   E6   Eb7   Dmaj7
I've gotta say I'm on my way ____ down.

Db   E6   Eb7   Dmaj7
God give me style and give me grace.

Db   E6   Eb7   Dmaj7
God put a smile upon my face. _____

Guitar Solo 1
| Db | E6 | Eb7 | Eb7 Dmaj7 |

| Db | E6 | Eb7 | Dmaj7 |

Verse 2

Db   E6   Eb7   Dmaj7
Where do we go to draw the line?

Db   E6   Eb7   Dmaj7
I've gotta say I've wasted all your time, honey, honey

Db   E6   Eb7   Dmaj7
Where do I go to fall from grace?

Db   E6   Eb7   Dmaj7
God put a smile upon your face. Yeah.

Chorus 1

                Amaj7   E6   F#add9   Amaj7
And ah _____ when you work it out I'm worse than you. _____

                                  E6   F#add9   Amaj7
Yeah, _____ when you work it out I wanted to. _____

                                  E6   F#add9   Amaj7
And ah _____ when you work out where to draw the line, _____

                E6   F#add9
Your guess is as good as mine.

Guitar Solo 2 | D♭ | E6 | E♭7 | E♭7   Dmaj7 |

| D♭ | E6 | E♭7 | Dmaj7   ‖

Verse 3

D♭   E6   E♭7   Dmaj7
    Where do we go nobody knows

D♭   E6   E♭7   Dmaj7
    Don't ever say you're on your way down

    D♭   E6   E♭7   Dmaj7
When God gave you style and gave you grace,

D♭   E6   E♭7   Dmaj7
    And put a smile upon your face, oh yeah.

Chorus 2

    Amaj7   E6   F#add9   Amaj7
And ah, when you work it out I'm worse than you. _____

                E6   F#add9   Amaj7
Yeah, when you work it out I wanted to. _____

                E6   F#add9   Amaj7
And ah, when you work out where to draw the line, _____

                E6   F#add9   D♭   E6   E♭7
Your guess is as good as mine. _____

        Dmaj7   D♭   E6   E♭7
It's as good as mine. _____

        Dmaj7   D♭   E6   E♭7
It's as good as mine. _____

        Dmaj7   D♭   E6
It's as good as mine. _____

E♭7
Na na na na na na na na na na

        Dmaj7   Amaj7   E6
It's as good as mine. _____

F#add9   Amaj7   E6
It's as good as mine. _____

F#add9   Amaj7   E6   F#add9
It's as good as mine. _____

Outro

D♭   E6   E♭7   Dmaj7
    Where do we go nobody knows

D♭   E6   E♭7   Dmaj7
    Don't ever say you're on your way down

    D♭   E6   E♭7   Dmaj7
When God gave you style and gave you grace

D♭   E6   E♭7   Dmaj7
    And put a smile upon your face.

HARDER TO BREATHE

WORDS & MUSIC BY ADAM LEVINE, JAMES VALENTINE, JESSE CARMICHAEL, MICKEY MADDEN & RYAN DUSICK

C#m   G#   B   F#   A/C#   C#m6

Verse 1

C#m
How dare you say that my behaviour is unacceptable

So condescending unnecessarily critical

I have the tendency of getting very physical

So watch your step 'cause if I do you'll need a miracle.

Verse 2

You drain me dry and make me wonder why I'm even here

The double vision I was seeing is finally clear

You want to stay but you know very well I want you gone,

Not fit to fuckin' tread the ground that I am walking on.

Chorus 1

                    G#   B   F#
When it gets cold outside and you got nobody to love
C#m   G#
    You'll understand what I mean when I say
          B   F#
There's no way we're gonna give up
C#m   G#   B
    And like a little girl cries in the face of a monster
         F#
That lives in her dreams
C#m   G#
    Is there anyone out there 'cause it's getting harder
       C#m
And harder to breathe.
C#m   N.C.
    Is there anyone out there 'cause it's getting harder and harder to breathe.

Verse 3

C#m

What you are doing is screwing things up inside my head

You should know better you never listened to a word I said

Clutching your pillow and writhing in a naked sweat

Hoping somebody someday will do you like I did.

Chorus 2   As Chorus 1

Solo   ‖ C#m A/C# | C#m6 A/C# | C#m A/C# | C#m6 A/C# ‖

Bridge

       C#m   A/C#
Does it kill, does it burn, is it painful to learn

        C#m6   A/C#
That it's me that has all the con - trol

       C#m   A/C#
Does it thrill, does it sting when you feel what I bring

        C#m6   A/C#
And you wish that you had me to hold

Chorus 3

C#m   G#   B   F#
When it gets cold outside and you got nobody to love

C#m   G#
You'll understand what I mean when I say

       B   F#
There's no way we're gonna give up

C#m   G#   B
And like a little girl cries in the face of a monster

       F#
That lives in her dreams

C#m   G#
Is there anyone out there 'cause it's getting harder

       C#m
And harder to breathe.

C#m   G#
Is there anyone out there 'cause it's getting harder

       C#m
And harder to breathe

C#m   N.C.
Is there anyone out there 'cause it's getting harder

And harder to breathe.

25

HAVE IT ALL

WORDS & MUSIC BY DAVE GROHL, TAYLOR HAWKINS, NATE MENDEL & CHRIS SHIFLETT

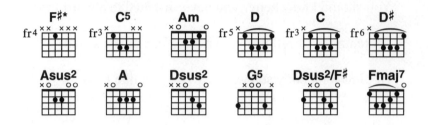

Intro

| F#* C5 F#* C5 | F#* C5 F#* C5 |

| F#* C5 F#* C5 | F#* C5 F#* C5 ‖

| Am | Am | D | C |

| Am | Am | D | C D D# ‖

| Am | Am | D | C D D# |

| Am | Am | D | C D D# ‖

| Am | Am | D | C D D# |

| Am | Am | D | C D ‖

Verse 1

Am   D C
You're my size I need to try you on

Am   D C
Someone in between the right and wrong

    Am   D C
Through everything, you kept your wings a - part

    Am   D C
Through everything, you stayed the same, hold on.

     Asus2 A
And when I've had enough

Pre-chorus 1

   Asus2
She drains me

     Dsus2
When I'm empty

   Asus2
She fills herself

   Dsus2
She takes it all

Chorus 1

G5 **Dsus2/F#**
In too deep

   Fmaj7 **A**
She's spilling over me

G5 **Dsus2/F#**
In too deep

   Fmaj7 **A**
She's spilling over me

     F#* C5 F#* C5 F#* C5 F#* C5 **Am**
Don't wanna ha - a - a - a - ave it all.

Link

| **Am** | **Am** | **D** | **C D D#** |

| **Am** | **Am** | **D** | **C D** ‖

Verse 2

Am   **D C**
Running through this maze you hold me in

Am   **D** **C**
Searching all these days to find the end

Am   **D** **C**
You're everything you're everything I'm not

  Am   **D** **C**
I'm anything I'm anyone you want.

    Asus2 A
And when I've had enough

Pre-chorus 2 As Pre-chorus 1

Chorus 2

G5   **Dsus2/F#**
In too deep

    Fmaj7   **A**
She's spilling over me

G5   **Dsus2/F#**
In too deep

    Fmaj7   **A**
She's spilling over me

                        F#* C5 F#* C5 F#*C5 F#*C5   **A**
Don't wanna ha - a - a - a - ave it all

F#* C5 F#*C5 F#*C5 F#*C5   **A**
Ha - a - a - a - ave it all

F#* C5 F#* C5 F#* C5 F#* C5 F#* C5 F#* C5 F#* C5   **(Am)**
Ha - a - a - a - a - a - a - a - ave it all.

Link 2
  | **Am** | **Am** | **D** | **C D D#** |

  | **Am** | **Am** | **D** | **C D**   ‖

Verse 3

Am   **D**   **C**
You're everything you're everything I'm not

    Am   **D**   **C** | **Asus2** | **A**   ‖
I'm anything I'm anyone you want.

Pre-chorus 3   As Pre-chorus 1

Chorus 3

G5   **Dsus2/F#**
In too deep

    Fmaj7   **A**
She's spilling over me,

G5   **Dsus2/F#**
In too deep

    Fmaj7   **A**
She's spilling over me,

G5   **Dsus2/F#**
In too deep

    Fmaj7   **A**
She's spilling over me,

G5   **Dsus2/F#**
In too deep

    Fmaj7   **A**
She's spilling over me

F#* C5 F#*C5 F#* C5 F#*C5 F#* C5 F#* C5 F#*C5 F#* C5   **(Am)**
Ha - a - a - a - a - a - a - a - ave it all.

Outro

| Am | Am | Am | Am C D D# |

| Am | Am | Am | Am C D D# ‖

| Am | Am | Am | Am C D D# |

| Am | Am | Am | Am C D D# ‖

| Am | Am | Am | Am C D D# |

| Am | Am | Am | Am C D D# ‖

| Am | Am | Am | Am C D D# |

| Am | Am | Am | Am C D D# ‖

$\frac{3}{4}$ | C D D# | C D D# | C D D# | C D D# |

| C D D# | C D D# | C D D# | C D D# ‖

HEY YA!

WORDS & MUSIC BY ANDRE BENJAMIN

G   C   D   E

Verse 1

        G
1, 2, 3, Uh!

          C
My baby don't mess around

Because she loves me so

      D   **E**
And this I know fo' sho' (Uh!)

G   **C**
  But does she really wanna

                D   **E**
Not to expect to see me walk out the do'?

G   **C**
  Don't try to fight the feeling

'Cause the thought alone

      D   **E**
Is killing me right now. (Uh!)

G   **C**
  Thank God for Mom and Dad

For sticking two together

      D   **E**
'Cause we don't know how.

C'mon!

Chorus 1

G C D E
Hey Ya! Hey Ya!

G C D E
Hey Ya! Hey Ya!

G C D E
Hey Ya! Hey Ya!

G C D E
Hey Ya! Hey Ya!

Verse 2

G
   You think you've got it

C
Oh, you think you've got it

But got it just don't get it

       D   E
'Til there's nothing at all. (Ah!)

G
   We get together

C
Oh, we get together

But separate's always better

       D   E
When there's feelings in - volved. (Oh!)

G   C
   If what they say is "nothing is forever"

Then what makes,

Then what makes,

       D
Then what makes,

       E
Then what makes,

Then what makes, (What makes? What makes?)

Love the exception?

G
   So why oh, why oh

C
Why oh, why oh, why oh

Are we so in denial

       D   E   N.C.
When we know we're not happy here?

             G   C
Chorus 2   Y'all don't want to hear me, you just want to dance,
            (Hey   Ya!)

   D E
(Hey Ya!)

                         G   C
Don't want to meet your daddy,   just want you in my Caddy
                 (Hey   Ya!)

       D   E
(Hey Ya!)

                                G   **C**
Don't want to meet your momma,   just want to make you come-a
                (Hey   Ya!)

D   **E**
   I'm,   I'm
(Hey   Ya!)

G   **C**   **D**   **E**
  I'm just being honest, I'm just being honest
(Hey   Ya!)   (Hey Ya!)

Verse 3

Hey! Alright now!

      G   **C**
Alright now, fellas! (Yeah!)

                              D E
Now what's cooler than being cool? (Ice cold!)

I can't hear ya!

                        G   **C**
I say what's, what's cooler than being cool? (Ice cold!)

                      D   **E**
Alright, alright, alright, alright, al - right, alright, al - right,

Alright, alright, alright, alright, alright, alright, alright,

     G   **C**
Okay now, ladies! (Yeah!)

                              D   **E**
Now we gon' break this thing down in just a few seconds

                      G
Now don't have me break this thing down for nothin!

  C
Now I wanna see y'all on y'all baddest behaviour!

D   **E**
Lend me some sugar!

I am your neighbour!

Ah! Here we go! Uh!

Breakdown

(Dbass)
Shake it, sh-shake it

(Cbass)
Shake it, sh-shake it

Shake it, sh-shake it

(Dbass)
Shake it, shake it

(Ebass)
Sh-shake it

(Dbass)
Shake it like a Polaroid picture (Hey ya!)

(Cbass)
Shake it, sh-shake it (Ok!)

Shake it, sh-shake it

(Dbass)
Shake it, shake it (Ok!)

(Ebass)
Shake it, sh-shake it (Shake it sugar!)

Shake it like a Polaroid picture

(Dbass)   **(Cbass)**
Now all Beyonce's and Lucy Lui's and baby dolls

(Dbass)   **(Ebass)**
   Get on the floor

(Git on the flo')

(Dbass) (Cbass)
You know what to do,

(Dbass)
You know what to do,

(Ebass)
   You know what to do.

Chorus 3

|: **G   C   D   E**
   Hey Ya! (Oh oh!) Hey Ya! (Oh oh!)
G   C   D   E
Hey Ya! (Oh oh!) Hey Ya! (Oh oh! Hey Ya!)
G   C   D   E
Hey Ya! (Oh oh!) Hey Ya! (Oh oh!)
G   C   D   E
Hey Ya! (Oh oh!) Hey Ya! (Oh oh!) :| *Repeat to fade*

33

HANDS DOWN

WORDS & MUSIC BY CHRISTOPHER CARRABBA

⑥ = E♭   ③ = G♭
⑤ = A♭   ② = B♭
④ = D♭   ① = E♭

Eadd9   E   Esus4add9   B*

E5   C#5   A5   D5

C#m   G#m   A   B5

Intro

| Eadd9 E | Eadd9 Esus4add9 Eadd9 |

| Eadd9 E | Eadd9 Esus4add9 Eadd9 |

| Eadd9 E | Eadd9 Esus4add9 Eadd9 |

| Eadd9 E | Eadd9 B* | B* ‖

Verse 1

E5   C#5   A5
Breathe in for luck, breathe in so deep
    B*   D5 C#5 E5
This air is blessed, you share with me
      C#5   A5
This night is wild, so calm and dull
        B*   D5 C#5 E5
These hearts they race from self cont - rol
     C#m   A5
Your legs are smooth as they graze mine
     B* N.C.   E
We're doing fine, we're doing nothing at all.

Chorus 1

                                                                   G#m
My hopes are so high that your kiss might kill me

           A   **G#m** **A** **G#m**
So won't you kill me, so I die happy.

E   **G#m**
   My heart is yours to fill or burst,

           A   **G#m**
To break or bury, or wear as jewellery

         A **G#m**   **E**
Which - ever you pre - fer.

Verse 2

                                  C#5
The words are hushed let's not get busted,

         A5   **B***   **D5** **C#5**
Just lay en - twined here undis - covered.

E5   **C#5**
Safe in here from all the stupid questions...

          A5
"Hey did you get some?"

         B*   **D5** **C#5**
"Man, that is so dumb."

E5   **C#5**
   Stay quiet, stay near, stay close

          A5 **N.C.**   **B*** **N.C.** **D5** **C#5**
They can't hear, so we can get some.

Chorus 2

E5   **G#m**
My hopes are so high that your kiss might kill me

          A   **G#m** **A** **G#m**
So won't you kill me, so I die happy.

E   **G#m**
   My heart is yours to fill or burst,

           A   **G#m**
To break or bury, or wear as jewellery

         A **G#m**   **(C#m)**
Which - ever you pre - fer.

Bridge

C#m   A5   E5
Hands down, this is the best day I can ever remember

    B5   C#5
I'll always remember the sound of the stereo

      A5   E5
The dim of the soft lights, the scent of your hair

      B5
That you twirled in your fingers

      C#5   N.C.   A5
And the time on the clock when we realized it was so late

      E5   B5
And this walk that we shared to - gether

    C#5   A5
The streets were wet and the gate was locked

   E5   B5
So I jumped it and I let you in,

      C#5   A5
And you stood at your door with your hands on my waist

      E5   B5
And you kissed me like you meant it,

    C#5   A5
And I knew, that you meant it,

    E5   B5
That you meant it, that you meant it,

    C#5   A5   E5
And I knew that you meant it, that you meant it.

I MISS YOU

WORDS & MUSIC BY MARK HOPPUS, TOM DELONGE & TRAVIS BARKER

B   D#m/A#   G#m7   E

Intro | N.C. | N.C. | B | D#m/A# | G#m7 | D#m/A# |

| B | D#m/A# | G#m7 | D#m/A# | B |

(I miss you, miss you)

| D#m/A# | G#m7 | D#m/A# ‖

Verse 1

   B   D#m/A#
Hel - lo there, the angel from my nightmare
 G#m7   D#m/A#
The shadow in the background of the morgue
         B   D#m/A#
The unsuspecting victim of darkness in the valley
   G#m7   D#m/A#
We can live like Jack and Sally if we want
          B
Where you can always find me
     D#m/A#
And we'll have Halloween on Christmas
   G#m7   D#m/A#
And in the night, we'll wish this never ends
       B
We'll wish this never ends.

Chorus 1

| B | B | E | E | B | B | E | E

(I miss you, miss you)

| B | B ‖

(I miss you, miss you.)

Verse 1

         B   D♯m/A♯
Where are you? And I'm so sorry

   G♯m7   D♯m/A♯
I cannot sleep I cannot dream to - night

                  B
I need somebody and always

            D♯m/A♯
This sick strange darkness

         G♯m7   D♯m/A♯
Comes creeping on so haunting every time

              B
And as I stared, I counted

     D♯m/A♯
The webs from all the spiders

G♯m7   D♯m/A♯
Catching things and eating their in - sides

             B
Like indecision to call you

     D♯m/A♯
And hear your voice of treason

       G♯m7   D♯m/A♯
Will you come home and stop this pain to - night

        (B)
Stop this pain tonight

Chorus 2

B
Don't waste your time on me you're already

   E
The voice inside my 'ead (I miss you, miss you)

B
Don't waste your time on me you're already

   E   B
The voice inside my 'ead (I miss you, miss you)

Instrumental ‖: G♯m7 | D♯m/A♯ | B | D♯m/A♯ :‖

38

Chorus 3

B
Don't waste your time on me you're already

    E
The voice inside my 'ead (I miss you, miss you)

B
Don't waste your time on me you're already

    E
The voice inside my 'ead (I miss you, miss you).

B
Don't waste your time on me you're already

    E
The voice inside my 'ead (I miss you, miss you)

B
Don't waste your time on me you're already

    E
The voice inside my 'ead (I miss you, miss you).

Outro

| **B** | **B** | ‖: **E** | **E** | **B** | **B** | :‖ |

(I miss you, miss you)

Repeat to fade

IN LOVE

WORDS & MUSIC BY CHRISTIAN DATSUN, DOLF DE DATSUN, MATT DATSUN & PHIL DATSUN

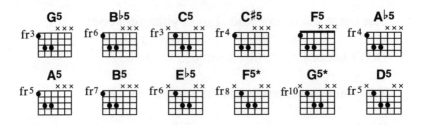

Intro   ‖: G5 B♭5 C5 | G5 B♭5 C5 | G5 B♭5 C5 C♯5 | C5 B♭5 F5 :‖ *Play 3 times*

Verse 1

G5
Hey, I feel lonely

                                                       B♭5 F5
But I got so many different women on my mind

        B♭5 C5
It's uncool,   to be kind.

G5
Why do you keep on running?

                                  B♭5 F5
Why do you keep on humming?

        B♭5 C5
It's uncool,   to be kind

Kinda, kinda like

Chorus 1

        G5   B♭5 C5
I'm in love (I'm in   love)

        G5   B♭5 C5
I'm in love (I'm in   love)

        G5   B♭5 C5   C♯5 | C5 B♭5 F5 ‖
I'm in love (I'm in   love)

        G5   B♭5 C5
I'm in love (I'm in   love)

        G5   B♭5 C5
I'm in love (I'm in   love)

        G5   B♭5 C5   C♯5 | C5 B♭5 F5 ‖
I'm in love (I'm in   love)

Verse 2   **G5**
Ooh, I believed ya

But when I saw you coming, I couldn't concede yeah
F5   **B♭5 C5**
  It's uncool,   to be kind
G5
Why do you keep on running?
                  B♭5 F5
Why do you keep on humming?
       B♭5 C5
It's uncool,   to be kind

Kinda, kinda like

Chorus 2   As Chorus 1

           G5
Link   Hey girl, when we say that we're in love
           C5
     We best believe that we're in love
           G5
     But I don't know

Don't know what I'm saying
A♭5   **A5 B♭5**   **B5**
Aaah!   Yeah!

Guitar solo   ‖: **C5 E♭5 F5*** | **G5* F5* C5** | **C5 E♭5 F5*** | **B♭5 F5* C5** :‖ *Play 3 times*

Bridge

     A♭5   **E♭5**   **C5**

I said oh, baby   this happens all of the time

   A♭5   **E♭5**   **D5**

And sugar yeah it's driving me wild, wild, wild!

Chorus 3   As Chorus 1

Outro

G5   **B♭5** **C5**

 I'm in love

D5   **B♭5** **G5**

 I'm in love

G5   **B♭5** **C5**   **C♯5** | **C5** **B♭5** **F5** ‖

 I'm in love

G5   **B♭5** **C5**

 I'm in love

D5   **B♭5** **G5**

 I'm in love

G5   **B♭5**   **C5**   **C♯5** | **C5** **B♭5** **F5** | **F5** | **F5** | **F5** | **F5** |

 I'm in   love

F5 | **F5** | **G5** ‖

It's kinda, kinda like I'm in love.

JUST BECAUSE

WORDS & MUSIC BY PERRY FARRELL, DAVE NAVARRO, CHRIS CHANEY, STEPHEN PERKINS & BOB EZRIN

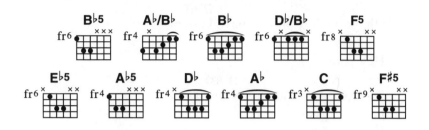

Intro | B♭5 | B♭5 | B♭5 | B♭5 |

| A♭/B♭ | A♭/B♭ | A♭/B♭ | A♭/B♭ ‖

| B♭5 | B♭5 | B♭5 | B♭5 |

| A♭/B♭ | A♭/B♭ | A♭/B♭ | A♭/B♭ ‖

         B♭5

Verse 1   If I were you

           A♭/B♭ **D♭/B♭**
I'd better watch out

A♭/B♭   **B♭5**
When was the last time

       A♭/B♭
You did anything

B♭   **B♭5**
Not for me

        A♭/B♭ **D♭/B♭**
Or anyone else

A♭/B♭   **B♭5**
Just be - cause

       A♭/B♭ | **A♭/B♭** | **A♭/B♭** | **B♭** ‖
Just be - cause

Chorus 1

B♭5
You,

                      D♭/B♭
Oh, you really should have known

    B♭5
Hey you!

                   D♭/B♭
You really should have known

F5   **E♭5**
Just be - cause

           B♭5
Just be - cause

| **B♭5** | **B♭5** | **B♭5** | **B♭5** | |

| **A♭/B♭** | **A♭/B♭** | **A♭/B♭** | **B♭** | ‖

Verse 2

            B♭5
You've got the most

              A♭/B♭ **D♭/B♭** **A♭/B♭**
Ahh, but nobody loves   you

      B♭5
Nobody has to

        A♭/B♭ | **A♭/B♭** | **A♭/B♭** | **B♭** ‖
Just be - cause

Chorus 2

B♭5
You,

                    D♭/B♭
You really should have known

    B♭5
Oh, you

                         D♭/B♭
I think you really should have known

F5   **E♭5**
Just be - cause

             B♭5
Just bec - a - a - ause

Bridge 1

| **A♭5** | **D♭** **A♭** | **B♭** | **B♭** | |
                             Oh yeah

| **A♭5** | **D♭** **A♭** | **C** | **C** | |
                     Oh, you better watch out

| **F♯5** | **F♯5** **F5** | **F5** | **F♯5** | **F5** | **F5** | **F5** | **⁶₄ F5** | ‖

44

Verse 3
              B♭5
When we first met
                  A♭/B♭   **D♭/B♭**
And we passed around gifts
A♭/B♭   **B♭5**
That was a long time, ago
              A♭/B♭ | **A♭/B♭** | **A♭/B♭** | **B♭** ‖
And you're feeling fit.

            B♭5
Chorus 3   Yeah you,

                    D♭/B♭
Oh, you really should have known
      B♭5
Yeah you,

                    D♭/B♭
Oh, you really should have known
F5   **E♭5**
Just be - cause
F5   **E♭5**
Just be - cause

            B♭5
Just beca - a - a -ause

  | **A♭5** | **D♭ A♭** | **B♭** | **B♭** |
Bridge 2   Oh yeah,
  | **A♭5**| | **D♭ A♭** | **C** | **A♭** | **D♭** ‖
              Oh, you better watch   out.

  | **F♯5** | **F♯5** | **F5** | **F5** | **F♯5** | **F5** | **F5** | **F5** | **F5** | **F5** ‖

LAST TRAIN HOME

WORDS & MUSIC BY IAN WATKINS, LEE GAZE, MIKE LEWIS, STUART RICHARDSON, MIKE CHIPLIN & JAMIE OLIVER

⑥ = D ③ = G
⑤ = A ②ⁱ = B
④ = D ①ⁱ = E

Chord diagrams: Cmaj7, Em, Dsus4add13, Dsus4, C5, E5, D5, A5, G5, F5

Intro

| Cmaj7 | Em | Dsus4add13 | Dsus4 ‖

One! Two! Three!

| C5 | E5 | D5 | D5 |

| C5 | E5 | D5 | D5 ‖

Verse 1

C5   E5   D5
To every broken heart in here

C5   E5
Love was once a part,

   D5
But now it's disappeared

           C5   E5   D5
She told me that it's all a part of the choices that you're making

          C5
Even when you think you're right

   E5   D5
You have to give to take.

Pre-chorus 1

        A5
But there's still tomorrow

   C5
For - get the sorrow

   G5   D5
And I can be on the last train home

       A5
Watch it pass the day

cont.

      C5
As it fades away

      G5
No more time to care

      D5
No more time,

     F5
To - day.

Chorus 1

      C5
But we sing

          E5
If we're going nowhere,

      D5
Yeah we sing

If it's not enough,

      C5
And we sing

         E5
Sing without a reason

      D5
To ever fall in love.

Verse 2

C5   **E5**   **D5**
  I wonder if you're listen - ing

      C5
Picking up on the signals

E5   **D5**
Sent back from with - in.

        C5   **E5**   **D5**
Sometimes it feels like I don't really know what's going on,

       C5   **E5**   **D5**
Time and time a - gain, it seems like everything is wrong in here.

Pre-chorus 2   As Pre-chorus 1

Chorus 2   As Chorus 1

Link | C5 | C5 | D5 | D5   ‖

                    C5
Chorus 3   But we sing
                          E5
             If we're going nowhere,
                      D5
             Yeah we sing

             If it's not enough
                      C5
             And we sing
                          E5
             Sing without a reason
                      D5
             To ever fall in love.
                      C5
             But we sing
                          E5
             If we're going nowhere
                      D5
             Yeah we sing

             If it's not enough
                      C5
             And we sing
                          E5
             Sing with out a reason
                      D5
             To never fall in love
                                    Cmaj7 | **Em** | **Dsus4add13** | **Dsus4** |
             To never fall in love a - gain
                                    Cmaj7 | **Em** | **Dsus4add13** | **Dsus4** |
             To never fall in love a - gain
                                    Cmaj7 | **Em** | **Dsus4add13** | **Dsus4** |
             To never fall in love a - gain

             | **Cmaj7** ‖

LITTLE KNOW IT ALL

WORDS & MUSIC BY IGGY POP, DERYCK WHIBLEY & GREIG NORI

⑥ = E♭ ③ = G♭
⑤ = A♭ ②ⁱ = B♭
④ = D♭ ① = E♭

F#5 E5 D5

A5 B5 C#5

Intro

‖: F#5 E5 F#5 E5 | D5 A5 | F#5 E5 F#5 E5 | D5 E5 |

| F#5 E5 F#5 E5 | D5 A5 | E5 | A5 B5 :‖

Verse 1

     F#5   E5 F#5 E5 D5   A5
I'm the kid that no one   knows,

  F#5 E5 F#5 E5 D5 E5
I live a life   I   never chose,

    F#5   E5 F#5 E5 D5   A5
But these thoughts in my   mind,

     E5   A5 B5
Are my own, my own

        F#5   E5 F#5 E5 D5   A5
I'm face to face with the un - known,

    F#5   E5 F#5 E5 D5   E5
My scary mo - vie   will be shown,

    F#5   E5 F#5 E5 D5 A5
I've got one e - vil   mind,

    E5   A5 B5
My own, my own.

Chorus 1

    F#5
We take from one another,

   D5
And never stop to wonder

   A5   E5
How it feels from the other side,

   F#5
But nothing lasts forever,

   D5
When stupid turns to clever,

A5   E5
Why are you sur - prised,

         D5   **A5**
Little know it all (little know it all)

E5   **F#5**
Ten bucks in my hand,

           D5   **A5**
Little know it all (little know it all)

    E5   **C#5**
Don't cry, I under - stand.

So...

Link 1 | **F#5 E5 F#5 E5 | D5 A5 | E5 | A5 B5** ‖

Verse 2
        F#5   **E5 F#5**   **E5 D5**   **A5**
I'm a target al - though   smart,

        F#5   **E5 F#5 E5** **D5 E5**
They got ammu - ni - tion   I got heart,

      F#5 E5 F#5 E5   **D5**   **A5**
I'm ana - lyzed and tagged,

         E5   **A5**   **B5**
Before I start

          F#5   **E5 F#5 E5 D5**   **A5**
So tell me who can I   re - spect,

  F#5   **E5 F#5 E5**   **D5**   **E5**
I feel the leash   a - round my neck,

    F#5   **E5 F#5 E5 D5**   **A5**
As I   find out the   shame,

      E5   **A5**   **B5**
In the game (in the game).

Chorus 2
     F#5
We take from one another,

    D5
And never stop to wonder

      A5   **E5**
How it feels from the other side,

     F#5
But nothing lasts forever,

       D5
When stupid turns to clever,

A5   **E5**
Why are you sur - prised,

      F#5 D5   **A5**   **E5**
And I feel like I've crawled outside the box

      F#5 D5   **A5**   **E5**
And I feel like I'm sleeping when I'm not.

| *Guitar solo* | |D5 | |A5 | |E5 | |F♯5 | | | |
| | |D5 | |A5 | |E5 | |E5 ‖ | |

Link 2		F♯5		D5		A5		E5		
				Looking for the real thing,					
		F♯5		D5		A5		E5		
				Looking for the real thing.					

Chorus 3

    F♯5
We take from one another,

    D5
And never stop to wonder

    A5   E5
How it feels from the other side,

    F♯5
But nothing lasts forever,

    D5
When stupid turns to clever,

A5   E5
Why are you sur - prised,

       D5   A5
Little know it all (little know it all)

E5   F♯5
Ten bucks in my hand,

       D5   A5
Little know it all (little know it all)

   E5   F♯5
Don't cry, I under - stand

       D5   A5
You little know it all (little know it all)

E5   F♯5
Ten bucks in my hand,

       D5   A5
Little know it all (little know it all)

   E5   F♯5
Don't cry I under - stand,

          D5 | A5 | E5 | A5 B5 E5 | E5 ‖
You'll never know it all.

LOVE WILL COME THROUGH

WORDS & MUSIC BY FRAN HEALY

Bm   G   D   F#7

x5

Intro   ‖: Bm   G | D   F#7 :‖

Verse 1

        Bm   G   D   F#7
If I told you a secret you won't tell a soul
           Bm   G   D   F#7
Will you hold it and keep it alive?
           Bm   G   D   F#7
'Cause it's burning a hole and I can't get to sleep
           Bm   G   D   F#7
And I can't live alone in this lie.

Pre-chorus

        Bm G D   F#7
So look up,   take it away
          Bm   G   D   F#7
Don't look da-da-da-down the mountain
          Bm   G   D   F#7
If the world isn't turning your heart won't return
        Bm   G   D   F#7
Anyone, anything, anyhow.

Chorus 1

        Bm G   D   F#7
So take me, don't leave me
Bm G   D   F#7
Take me, don't leave me
Bm G D   F#7
Ba - by, love will come through
          Bm   G   D   F#7
It's just waiting for you.

Verse 2

      Bm   **G**   **D**   **F♯7**
Well I stand at the crossroads of high roads and low roads

      Bm **G**   **D**   **F♯7**
And I got a feeling it's right

      Bm   **G**   **D**   **F♯7**
If it's real what I'm feeling, there's no make-believing

      Bm   **G**   **D**   **F♯7**
The sound of the wings of the flight

      Bm
Of a dove.

Pre-chorus 2   As Pre-chorus 1

Chorus 2   As Chorus 1

Interlude   ‖: **Bm** | **G** | **D** | **F♯7** | **Bm** | **G** | **D** | **F♯7** :‖

Bridge

          Bm
Oh look up take it away

N.C.
Don't look da da da down

      Bm   **G**   **D**   **F♯7**
If the world isn't turning your heart won't return

      Bm **G**   **D**   **F♯7**
Anyone, anything, anyhow.

Chorus 3   As Chorus 1

Outro

Bm G D   **F♯7**
      Love will come through

Bm G D   **F♯7**
      Love will come through

Bm G D   **F♯7**
      Love will come through.

| **Bm G** | **D F♯7** | **Bm** | ‖

LOSE YOURSELF

WORDS & MUSIC BY MARSHALL MATHERS, JEFF BASS & LUIS RESTO

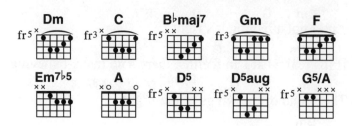

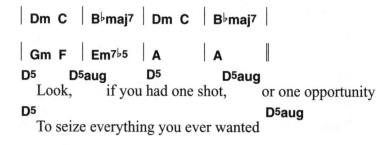

Intro

| Dm C | B♭maj7 | Dm C | B♭maj7 |

| Gm F | Em7♭5 | A | A ‖

D5   D5aug   D5   D5aug
   Look,   if you had one shot,   or one opportunity

D5
   To seize everything you ever wanted   D5aug

For one moment.

D5   D5aug   G5/D D5 D5aug G5/D D5
   Would you capture it or just let it slip?

Verse 1

          D5
Yo, his palms are sweaty, knees weak, arms are heavy
          D5aug
There's vomit on his sweater already, mom's spaghetti
          D5
He's nervous, but on the surface he looks calm and ready
          D5aug
To drop bombs, but he keeps on forgetting
              D5
What he wrote down, the whole crowd goes so loud
        D5aug
He opens his mouth, but the words won't come out,
        D5
He's chokin', how everybody's chokin' now,
        D5aug   G5/D D5 D5aug G5/D D5
The clock's run out, time's up over,   blaow!

Snap back to reality, oh there goes gravity

D5aug
Oh, there goes Rabbit, he choked

         D5
He's so mad, but he won't give up that easy

            D5aug
No, he won't have it, he knows his whole back city's ropes

        D5
It don't matter, he's dope.

He knows that, but he's broke

           D5aug
He's so stacked that he knows

When he goes back to his mobile home, that's when it's

D5
Back to the lab again yo,

This whole rap city

    D5aug   **G5/D D5 D5aug G5/D D5**
He better go capture this moment and hope it   don't pass   him.

         D5
Chorus 1   You better lose yourself in the music, the moment

    D5aug
You own it, you better never let it go,

       D5
You only get one shot, do not miss your chance to blow

         D5aug
This oppor - tunity comes once in a lifetime yo.

      D5
You better lose yourself in the music, the moment

     D5aug
You own it, you better never let it go

       D5
You only get one shot, do not miss your chance to blow

        D5aug   **G5/D D5**   **D5aug G5/D D5**
This oppor - tunity comes once in a life - time (you   bet - ter...)

Verse 2

D5
His soul's escaping, through this hole that it's gaping

D5aug
This world is mine for the taking

D5
Make me King, as we move toward a, new world order

D5aug   D5
A normal life is borin', but superstardom's close to post mortem

D5aug
It only grows harder, only grows hotter

He blows us all over these ho's is all on him

D5aug
Coast to coast shows, he's know as the globetrotter

G5/D D5   D5aug G5/D   D5
Lone - ly   roads, God   on - ly knows.

He's grown farther from home, he's no father

D5aug
He goes home and barely knows his own daughter

D5
But hold your nose 'cause here goes the cold water

D5aug
These ho's don't want him no mo, he's cold product

D5
They moved on to the next schmoe who flows

D5aug
He nose dove and sold nada

D5
So the soap opera is told and unfolds

D5aug
I suppose it's old partner, but the beat goes on,

G5/D   D5   D5aug G5/D D5
Da da dum   da dum da   da   da da

Chorus 2

D5
You better lose yourself in the music, the moment

D5aug
You own it, you better never let it go

D5
You only get one shot, do not miss your chance to blow

D5aug
This oppor - tunity comes once in a lifetime yo.

cont.

D5
You better lose yourself in the music, the moment

D5aug
You own it, you better never let it go

D5
You only get one shot, do not miss your chance to blow

D5aug   **G5/D D5** **D5aug** **G5/D** **D5**
This oppor - tunity comes once in a life - time. (You bet - ter...)

Verse 3

D5
No more games, I'ma change what you call rage

D5aug
Tear this mothafuckin' roof off like two dogs caged

D5
I was playin' in the beginnin', the mood all changed

D5aug
I been chewed up and spit out and booed off stage.

D5
But I kept rhymin' and stepwritin the next cypher

D5aug
Best believe somebody's payin' the pied piper

D5   **D5aug**
All the pain inside amplified by the fact

     G5/D D5 **D5aug G5/D** **D5**
That I can't get by with my nine to   five

D5aug
And I can't provide the right type of life for my family

D5
'Cause man, these goddam food stamps don't buy diapers

D5aug
And it's no movie, there's no Mekai Pfeiffer, this is my life

D5
And these times are so hard and it's getting even harder

D5aug
Tryin' to feed and water my seed, plus

D5
Teeter-totter caught up between trying to be a father and a pre-madonna

D5aug
Baby mama drama's screamin' on and

 G5/D **D5** **D5aug** **G5/D D5**
Too much for me to wan - na

cont. Stay in one spot, another jam or not

     D5aug
Has gotten me to the point, I'm like a snail

     D5
I've got to formulate a plot or I end up in jail or shot

    D5aug   **D5**
Suc - cess is my only mothafuckin' option, failure's not.

Mom, I love you, but this trailer's got to go

D5aug
I cannot grow old in Salem's lot

    D5
So here I go is my shot.

                                     D5aug   **G5/D** **D5**
Feet fail me not or not this may be the only opportunity that I got.
D5aug **G5/D** **D5**
You   bet - ter

     D5
Chorus 3   You better lose yourself in the music, the moment

     D5aug
You own it, you better never let it go

     D5
You only get one shot, do not miss your chance to blow

       D5aug
This oppor - tunity comes once in a lifetime yo.

     D5
You better lose yourself in the music, the moment

     D5aug
You own it, you better never let it go

      D5
You only get one shot, do not miss your chance to blow

      D5aug   **G5/D D5**   **D5aug G5/D D5**
This oppor - tunity comes once in a life -   time. (You   bet - ter...)

    D5aug   **D5aug**
Outro   You can do anything you set your mind to, man.

D5	**D5aug**	**D5**	**D5aug**	

D5	**D5aug G5/D D5 D5aug G5/D**

D5	**D5aug**	**D5**	**D5aug**	

D5	**D5aug**	**D5**	**D5aug G5/D D5 D5aug G5/D**

Fade out over last 8 bars

NUMB

WORDS & MUSIC BY CHESTER BENNINGTON, MIKE SHINODA, ROB BOURDON, JOSEPH HAHN, BRAD DELSON & DAVID FARRELL

⑥ = D♭ ③ = G♭
⑤ = A♭ ②ￜ= B♭
④ = D♭ ① = E♭

G5 (fr5) E♭5 B♭5 (fr8)

F5 A5 (fr7) D5 C5 (fr10)

Intro   ‖: G5 | E♭5 | B♭5 | F5 :‖

Verse 1

G5   E♭5
   I'm tired of being what you want me to be
B♭5   F5
Feeling so faithless lost under the surface,
G5   E♭5
   Don't know what you're ex - pecting of me
  B♭5   F5
Put under the pressure of walking in your shoes.

Pre-chorus 1

E♭5   G5   F5
  (Caught in the under - tow, just caught in the undertow)
   G5   A5 B♭5   D5
Every step that I take is an - other mis - take to you
E♭5   G5   F5
  (Caught in the under - tow just caught in the undertow).

Chorus 1

G5   E♭5   B♭5
I've become so numb, I can't feel you there
        F5   G5
I've become so tired, so much more a - ware.
     E♭5   B♭5
I'm becoming this, all I want to do,
      F5   G5
Is be more like me and be less like you.

Verse 2

Eb5
Can't you see that you're smothering me
Bb5   F5
Holding too tightly a - fraid to lose control,
G5   Eb5
   'Cause everything that you thought I would be
   Bb5   F5
Has fallen apart right in front of you.

Pre-chorus 2

Eb5   G5   F5
   (Caught in the under - tow just caught in the undertow)
    G5   A5 Bb5   D5
Every step that I take is an - other mis - take to you,
Eb5   G5   F5
   (Caught in the under - tow just caught in the undertow)
     G5   A5   Bb5   D5
And every second I waste is more than I can take.

Chorus 2

G5   Eb5   Bb5
I've become so numb, I can't feel you there
      F5   G5
I've become so tired, so much more a - ware,
     Eb5   Bb5
I'm becoming this, all I want to do
     F5   Eb5
Is be more like me and be less like you.

Bridge

    F5
And I know,
    G5   A5   Bb5   D5   Eb5
I may end up   fail - ing   too
    F5
But I know
      D5
You were just like me with someone disappointed in you.

Chorus 3

G5   Eb5   Bb5

I've become so numb, I can't feel you there,

             F5   G5

I've become so tired, so much more a - ware.

           Eb5   Bb5

I'm becoming this, all I want to do

           C5   F5   (G5)

Is be more like me and be less like you.

Chorus 4

G5   Eb5   Bb5

I've become so numb, I can't feel you there

                    F5

(I'm tired of being what you want me to be),

G5   Eb5   Bb5

I've become so numb, I can't feel you there

                    F5

(I'm tired of being what you want me to be).

Outro | G5 | Eb5 | Bb5 | F5   ‖

MAYBE TOMORROW

WORDS & MUSIC BY KELLY JONES, RICHARD JONES & STUART CABLE

$E\flat maj^7$ Cm   Gm $Fsus^2$ D^7 F $Csus^2$ $Fmaj^9$

Intro

$E\flat maj^7$ Cm
‖: Ooh, bap a-ooh, ooh, bap a-ooh,

Gm $Fsus^2$
Ooh, bap a-ooh, ooh, bap a-ooh. :‖

Verse 1

$E\flat maj^7$
    I've been down and I'm wondering why

Cm
These little black clouds keep a-walking around

Gm
With me

$Fsus^2$
With me.

$E\flat maj^7$
    It wastes time and I'd rather be high

Cm
Think I'll walk me outside and buy a rainbow smile

Gm
But be free,

$Fsus^2$
They're all free.

Chorus 1

$E\flat maj^7$ Cm
    So maybe tomorrow

Gm $Fsus^2$
I'll find my way___ home

$E\flat maj^7$ Cm
    So maybe tomorrow

Gm $Fsus^2$
I'll find my way___ home.

Verse 2

E♭maj7
   I look around at a beautiful life

         Cm
I've been the upper side of down, been the inside of out

      Gm   Fsus2
But we breathe, we breathe.

E♭maj7
   I wanna breeze and an open mind

       Cm
I wanna swim in the ocean,

              Gm   Fsus2
Wanna take my time for me, all me.

Chorus 2

‖: E♭maj7   Cm
       So maybe tomorrow

         Gm   Fsus2
I'll find my way___ home

E♭maj7   Cm
   So maybe tomorrow

         Gm   Fsus2
I'll find my way___ home. :‖

Guitar solo

‖: Cm | D7 | Gm | Fmaj9 :‖

| G5 | G5 | G5 | G5 | |
Ooh,   ooh,   ooh,   ooh.

Link

| E♭maj7 | Cm | Gm | Gm |

Chorus 3   As Chorus 2

Outro

| E♭maj7 | Cm | Gm | Fsus2 |

| E♭maj7 | Cm | Gm | Fsus2 |

                           Na, na, na,
| Gm | E♭maj7 | Gm | Fsus2 | |
Na, na, na, na,   na, na, na, na na, na, na, na, na, na, na

| Gm | Gm | Gm | Fsus2 | E♭maj7 ‖
Na. Oh._____ Oh,____ oh, ah oh.

MS. JACKSON

WORDS & MUSIC BY ANTWAN PATTON, ANDRE BENJAMIN & DAVID SHEATS

Cmaj⁷   D   Em

Intro

| Cmaj⁷ | Cmaj⁷ | Cmaj⁷ | D | |

| Em | Em | D | D ||

Chorus 1

Cmaj⁷
    I'm sorry Ms. Jackson

      D
I am for real,

Em
Never meant to make your daughter cry

D
I apologize a trillion times.

Cmaj⁷
    I'm sorry Ms. Jackson

      D
I am for real

Em
Never meant to make your daughter cry

D
I apologize a trillion times.

Link 1

| Cmaj⁷ | Cmaj⁷ | Cmaj⁷ | D | |

| Em | Em | D | D ||

Chorus 2   As Chorus 1

Verse 1

Cmaj7
Me and your daughter

                    D
Got a special thing go - ing on

Em
You say it's puppy love

D
We say it's fully grown.

Cmaj7
Hope that we feel this,

              D
Feel this way forev - er

Em
You can plan a pretty picnic

        D
But you can't predict the weather.

Link 2

| Cmaj7 | Cmaj7 | Cmaj7 | D | | Em | Em | D | D ‖

Can't predict the weather...

Chorus 3   As Chorus 1

Verse 2   As Verse 1

Outro

Cmaj7
Hope that we feel this,

             D
Feel this way forev - er,

Em
You can plan a pretty picnic

        D
But you can't predict the weather...

| Cmaj7 | Cmaj7 | Cmaj7 | D | | Em | Em | D | D ‖

Can't predict the weather...

Cmaj7
    I'm sorry Ms. Jackson...

ONE BIG HOLIDAY

WORDS & MUSIC BY JIM JAMES

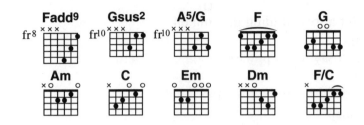

Intro

‖:Fadd⁹ | Gsus² | A⁵/G | A⁵/G |

| Fadd⁹ | Gsus² | A⁵/G | A⁵/G :‖ *Play 3 times*

| F | G | Am | Am ‖

‖:F | G | Am | Am |

| F | G | Am | Am :‖

Verse 1

C   F
  Wakin' up feelin'   good and limber
Em   Dm
  When the telephone it ring,
C   F
  Was a bad man from   California
Em   Dm
  Tellin' of a stone he'd bring.

Link 1

| Em | Em | Dm | Dm | G | G ‖

Chorus 1

          F/C G   Am
And of   better days
          F/C G   Am
From this town,   we'd esc - ape
             F/C G   Am
If we holler loud   and make our way
          F/C G   Am
We'd all live one big holi - day

Verse 2

    C   F
So we listened and   up the river
Em   Dm
And recorded all the sounds
C   F
Was some shakin' and some   record playin'
Em   Dm
All the leather kids were loud.

Link 2

Em	Em	Dm	Dm	
G	G	G	G	‖
F	G	Am	Am	‖

Solo

‖: F | G | Am | Am | |
| F | G | Am | Am | :‖ *Play 7 times*

Outro

Fadd⁹	Gsus²	A5/G	A5/G	
Fadd⁹	Gsus²	A5/G	A5/G	‖
Fadd⁹	Gsus²	A5/G	A5/G	A5/G	A5/G	‖

ONE HORSE TOWN

WORDS BY CONOR DEASY
MUSIC BY CONOR DEASY, KEVIN HORAN, PÁDRAIC McMAHON, DANIEL RYAN & BEN CARRIGAN

A   Asus4   B   E/B   D

Em   G   F#m   Bsus4   E   G#m

Intro

| A | A | Asus4 | Asus4 |

| Asus4 | A | Asus4 | A ||

Verse 1

       B   **E/B**
Yeah you're burnin',

       B   **E/B**
Oh you're burnin' my ears

                Asus4 | **A** | **Asus4** | **A** |
With your travel tales.

       B   **E/B**
But my in-laws,

          B
Oh baby, my in-laws,

          E/B   **Asus4** | **A** | **Asus4** | **A** |
Well they're tryin' to tie a young man down.

Chorus 1

D   **Em**   **A**
   Oh I never should've settled down,

G   **D**
Hanging around in a one horse town,

     F#m   **A**
When everyone started sleeping a - round.

D   **Em**   **A**
Well I never should've settled down,

G   **D**
Hanging around in a one horse town,

     F#m   **A**   **Asus4**
When everyone started sleeping a - round.

Link 1 | **Asus⁴** | **A** | **Asus⁴** | **A** ‖

               B   **E/B**

Verse 2   But this feeling

               B

Oh, that I'm feeling,

         E/B   **Asus⁴** | **A** | **Asus⁴** | **A** |

You're praying on a tender heart

           B   **E/B**

So this evening

              B

Oh baby, I'm leaving

         E/B   **Asus⁴** | **A** | **Asus⁴** | **A** |

On a one way ticket to - night.

Chorus 2   As Chorus 1

Link 2   As Link 1

Link 3 | **Bsus⁴** | **B** | **Bsus⁴** | **B** ‖

                                     Oh, oh, oh!

       E   **F♯m**   **B**

Chorus 4   Well my friends oh don't go settle down,

      A   **E**

Hanging around in a one horse town

          G♯m   **B**

When everyone started sleeping a - round.

      E   **F♯m**   **B**

'Guess I never should've settled down,

             A   **E**

You see, hanging around in a one horse town

          G♯m   **B**   **E**

Does nothing for your state of mind.

PIN

WORDS & MUSIC BY KAREN O, NICHOLAS ZINNER & BRIAN CHASE

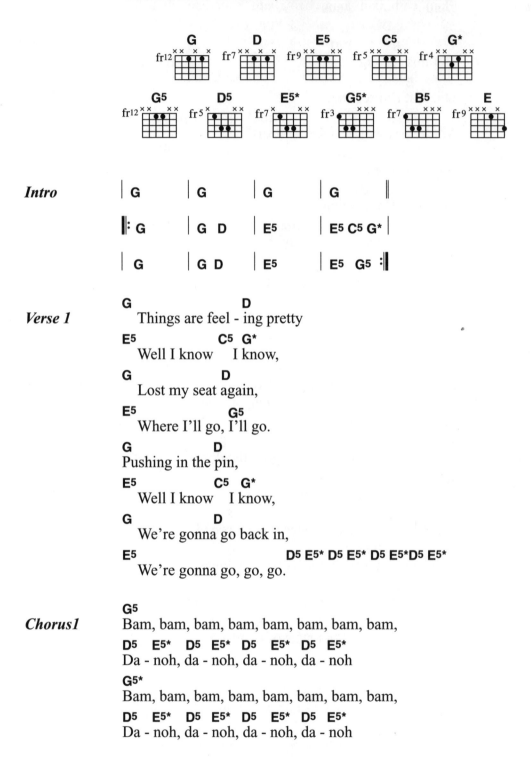

Intro

| G | G | G | G ‖

‖: G | G D | E5 | E5 C5 G* |

| G | G D | E5 | E5 G5 :‖

Verse 1

G   D
   Things are feel - ing pretty

E5   C5 G*
   Well I know   I know,

G   D
   Lost my seat again,

E5   G5
   Where I'll go, I'll go.

G   D
Pushing in the pin,

E5   C5 G*
   Well I know   I know,

G   D
   We're gonna go back in,

E5   D5 E5* D5 E5* D5 E5*D5 E5*
   We're gonna go, go, go.

Chorus 1

G5
Bam, bam, bam, bam, bam, bam, bam, bam,

D5   E5*   D5 E5* D5 E5* D5 E5*
Da - noh, da - noh, da - noh, da - noh

G5*
Bam, bam, bam, bam, bam, bam, bam, bam,

D5   E5*   D5 E5* D5 E5* D5 E5*
Da - noh, da - noh, da - noh, da - noh

cont.

G5*
Bam, bam, bam, bam, bam, bam, bam, bam, bam,

D5 E5* D5 E5* D5 E5* D5 E5*
Da - noh, da - noh, da - noh, da - noh

G5*   **D5**   **B5**
Bam, bam, bam, bam, bam, bam, bam, bam, bam!

Instr.

| **B5** | **B5** | **B5** | **B5** | **B5** | **B5** | |

| **B5** | **B5** | **E5** | **E5** | **E** | **E** | ‖

Verse 2

G   **D**
I like to sleep with them,

E5   **C5**   **G***
   Pushing in the pin

G   **D**
I like to sleep with them,

E5   **G5**
   Well I know I know,

G   **D**
   We're gonna go back in,

E5   **C5**   **G***
   We're gonna go,   go, go

G   **D**
   We're gonna go back in,

E5   **D5 E5* D5 E5* D5 E5*D5 E5***
   We're gonna go, go, go.

Chorus 2

G5
Bam, bam, bam, bam, bam, bam, bam, bam,

D5 E5* D5 E5* D5 E5* D5 E5*
Da - noh, da - noh, da - noh, da - noh

G5*
Bam, bam, bam, bam, bam, bam, bam, bam,

D5 E5* D5 E5* D5 E5* D5 E5*
Da - noh, da - noh, da - noh, da - noh

G5*
Bam, bam, bam, bam, bam, bam, bam, bam, bam,

D5 E5* D5 E5* D5 E5* D5 E5*
Da - noh, da - noh, da - noh, da - noh

G5*   **D5**   **E**   **E5***
Bam, bam, bam, bam, bam, bam, bam, bam, bam!

RUN

WORDS & MUSIC BY GARY LIGHTBODY, JONATHAN QUINN, MARK McCLELLAND, NATHAN CONNOLLY & IAIN ARCHER

Am	F/A	G5	Gsus4	C	G	F

Intro

‖: Am F/A | G5 Gsus4 G5 | Am F/A | G5 Gsus4 G5 :‖

Verse 1

        Am   F/A G5   Gsus4 G5
I'll sing it one last time for   you

         Am   F/A G5   Gsus4 G5
Then we really have to   go

           Am   F/A   G5 Gsus4 G5
You've been the only thing that's right

        Am   F/A G5   Gsus4 G5
In all I've   done.

Verse 2

        Am   F/A G5   Gsus4 G5
And I can barely look at you

        Am   F/A G5   Gsus4 G5
But every single time I   do

          Am   F/A   G5 Gsus4 G5
I know we'll make it an - y - where

        Am   F/A G5   Gsus4 G5
Away from   here.

Chorus 1

  C
   Light up, light up

    G
As if you have a choice

         Am
Even if you cannot hear my voice

        F |F |
I'll be right beside you dear

C
  Louder, louder

      G
And we'll run for our lives

        Am
I can hardly speak I understand

           F |F |
Why you can't raise your voice to say.

Link | Am F/A | G5 Gsus4 G5 | Am F/A | G5 Gsus4 G5 ‖

           Am   F/A   G5   Gsus4 G5

Verse 3   To think I might not see those eyes

                Am   F/A   G5 Gsus4 G5

    It makes it so hard not to   cry

                Am   F/A   G5 Gsus4 G5

    And as we say our long good - byes

             Am   F/A G5   Gsus4 G5

    I nearly do.

Chorus 2   As Chorus 1

    C

Chorus 3   Slower, slower

             G

    We don't have time for that

                  Am

    All I want is to find an easier way

               F

    To get out of our little heads.

    C

    Have heart my dear

           G

    We're bound to be afraid

             Am

    Even if it's just for a few days

             F | F |

    Making up for all this mess.

Solo   ‖: C | C | G | G | Am | Am | F | F :‖

    C

Outro   Light up, light up

         G

    As if you have a choice

             Am

    Even if you cannot hear my voice

             G F | F | C ‖

    I'll be right beside you dear.

SCHOOL OF ROCK

WORDS & MUSIC BY MIKE WHITE & SAMMY JAMES, JR.

D	Dsus4	Cadd9	G/B	G	E

Intro ‖: D | Dsus4 | D | Dsus4 :‖ *Play 3 times*

‖: D | Cadd9 | G/B | Cadd9 :‖

Verse 1

D   Cadd9
Baby we was makin' straight A's,

G/B   Cadd9
But we was stuck in the dumb days.

D   Cadd9
Don't take much to memo - rize your life,

G/B   Cadd9
I feel like I've been hyp - notisized.

Pre-chorus 1

        D   Cadd9
And then that magic man, he come to town.

       G/B   Cadd9
Woo - wee! He done spun my head around.

           D   Cadd9   G
He said, "Re - cess is in session, two and two make five."

And now baby oh, I'm alive.

Oh yeah!

I - I'm alive.

Chorus 1

              D   **E**
And if you wanna be the teacher's pet,

        G   **D**
Well, baby you just better for - get it.

D   **E**
   Rock got no reason, rock got no rhyme.

G
   You better get me to school on time.

Ah yeah,

Yeah!

Guitar solo   ‖: **D** | **Cadd⁹** | **G/B** | **Cadd⁹** :‖

               D   **Cadd⁹**
Verse 2   Oh you know I was on the honour roll.

G/B   **Cadd⁹**
   Got good grades, ain't got no soul.

D   **Cadd⁹**
   Raised my hand before I could speak my mind.

G/B   **Cadd⁹**
   I'd been biting my tongue too many times.

              D   **Cadd⁹**
Pre-chorus 2   And then that magic man said to obey (Uh-huh)

               G/B   **Cadd⁹**
"Do what magic man do. Not what magic man say."

D   **Cadd⁹**
   Now can I please have the at - tention of the class.

G
   Today's assignment

A-hem,

Kick some ass!

Chorus 2

           D   **E**
And if you wanna be the teacher's pet,
    G   **D**
Well, baby you just better for - get it.
D   **E**
  Rock got no reason,   Rock got no rhyme,
G
  You better get me to school on time.
          D   **E**
And if you wanna sbe the teacher's pet,
    G   **D**
Well, baby you just better for - get it.
D   **E**
  Rock got no reason, rock got no rhyme,
G
  You better get me to school on time.

Alright!

Yeah!

Instrumental   ‖: **D** | **Dsus4** | **D** | **Dsus4** :‖ *Play 3 times*

               ‖: **D** | **Cadd9** | **G/B** | **Cadd9** :‖

Verse 3

D **Cadd9**
  This is my final exam.
G/B   **Cadd9**
  Now, y'all know who I am.
D   **Cadd9**
  I might not be that perfect son.
G/B   **Cadd9**
  But you'll be rockin' when I'm done.

Outro | **D** | **Cadd9** | **G/B** | **Cadd9** |

               | **D** | **Cadd9** | **G/B** | **Cadd9** ‖

               | **D** | **Cadd9** | **G/B** | **Cadd9** |

               | **D** | **Cadd9** | **G** | **G** | **G** | **G**   ‖

               | **D** | **D** | **Cadd9** | **Cadd9** |

             | **G** | **G** | **G** | **G** | **G**   ‖

SO ALIVE

WORDS & MUSIC BY RYAN ADAMS & JOHNNY T. YERINGTON

E   G#m7   C#m7   Asus2   Esus4   C#m7/G#   Eadd9

Intro
```
|: E      | E      | G#m7   | G#m7   |

| C#m7   | C#m7   | Asus2  | Asus2  :|
```

Verse 1

E   Esus4 E   G#m7
Today   I watched the boats

                  C#m7
Moving through the harbour

        Asus2
Walking on water

              E
In your arms I'd stay

Esus4 E G#m7
For - ever   if I could

            C#m7
Forever if I may

                  Asus2
Keeps me in your thoughts, don't disappear.

Chorus 1

E   G#m7
I am on your side

        C#m7
Am so a - live

        Asus2
Am so a - live, it isn't real.

Verse 2

E   Esus4 E   G#m7
If this is how I feel

            C#m7
Then nothing now is true

                Asus2   E
And nothing now can ever be taken away from you.

        G#m7
Sinking in the past

cont.
                                              C#m7
The things that shouldn't last
                         Asus2
Just put to bed and stand beside me,

Stand beside me.

E   **G#m7**
Chorus 2   Always on your side
            C#m7
I'm on your side
            Asus2
And so a - live it isn't real.
E   **G#m7**
I am on your side
            C#m7
Am so a - live
            Asus2
Am so a - live

Am so alive.

Instrumental ‖: **E** | **E** | **C#m7/G#** | **C#m7/G#** |

            | **C#m7** | **C#m7** | **Asus2** | **Asus2** :‖

E   **G#m7**
Outro   I am on your side
            C#m7
On your side
            Asus2
I'm on your side,
            E
On your side
            G#m7
On your side
            C#m7
And so a - live
            Asus2
And so a - live.

Outro

        E   G#m7
So alive   a - live

      C#m7   Asus2
A - live, a - live

       E   G#m7
A - live,   a - live

      C#m7   Asus2
A - live, a - live

| E | E | G#m7 | G#m7 |

| C#m7 | C#m7 | Asus2 | Asus2 ‖

E   G#m7
I am on your side

     C#m7
On your side

       Asus2
I'm on your side

     Eadd9
On your side.

SOMEWHERE ONLY WE KNOW

WORDS & MUSIC BY TIM RICE-OXLEY, TOM CHAPLIN & RICHARD HUGHES

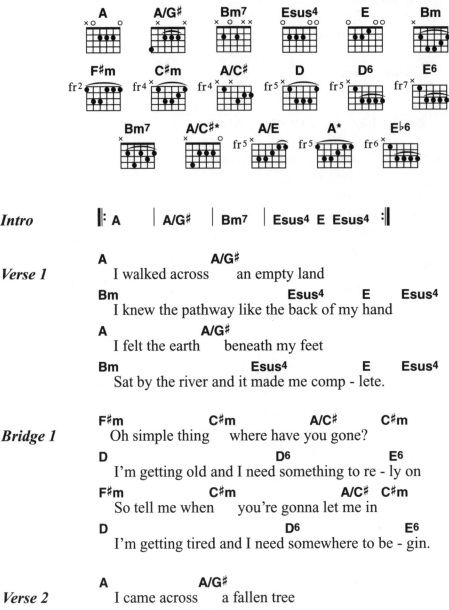

Intro

‖: A | A/G# | Bm7 | Esus4 E Esus4 :‖

Verse 1

A   A/G#
I walked across   an empty land
Bm   Esus4   E   Esus4
I knew the pathway like the back of my hand
A   A/G#
I felt the earth   beneath my feet
Bm   Esus4   E   Esus4
Sat by the river and it made me comp - lete.

Bridge 1

F#m   C#m   A/C#   C#m
Oh simple thing   where have you gone?
D   D6   E6
I'm getting old and I need something to re - ly on
F#m   C#m   A/C# C#m
So tell me when   you're gonna let me in
D   D6   E6
I'm getting tired and I need somewhere to be - gin.

Verse 2

A   A/G#
I came across   a fallen tree
Bm   Esus4   E   Esus4
I felt the branches of it looking at me
A   A/G#
Is this the place   we used to love
Bm   Esus4   E   Esus4
Is this the place that I've been dreaming of?

Bridge 2   As Bridge 1

Chorus 1

Bm7   **A/C#***   **A/E**
   And if you have a minute why don't we go

Bm7   **A/C#***   **A/E**
   Talk about it somewhere only we know

Bm7   **A/C#***   **A/E**
   This could be the end of every - thing

D6
So why don't we go

D6   **A***
Somewhere only we know.

Link 1

D6 **E6**   **D6** **E6** **Bm7/E** **E6**
   Somewhere only we know.___

Bridge 3   As Bridge 1

Chorus 2

Bm7   **A/C#***   **A/E**
   And if you have a minute why don't we go

Bm7   **A/C#***   **A/E**
   Talk about it somewhere only we know

Bm7   **A/C#***   **A/E**
   This could be the end of every - thing

D6
So why don't we go

D6   **A***
So why don't we   go.

Outro | **Bm7** | **A/C#*** **A/E** | **Bm7** | **A/C#*** **A/E** ‖

Bm7   **A/C#***   **A/E**
   This could be the end of every - thing

D6
So why don't we go

E6   **A***
Somewhere only we know

D6   **E6**   **E♭6** **D6**
   Somewhere only we kno - ow

E6   **D6** **D** **A***
Somewhere only we know.__

STACY'S MOM

WORDS & MUSIC BY ADAM SCHLESINGER & CHRIS COLLINGWOOD

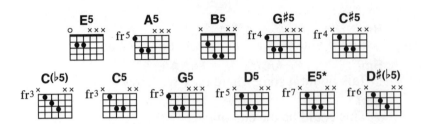

Intro

| E5 A5 | B5 A5 | E5 A5 | B5 A5 ‖

E5   A5   B5   A5
Stacy's mom has got it goin' on,

E5   A5   B5   A5
Stacy's mom has got it goin' on,

E5   A5   B5   A5
Stacy's mom has got it goin' on,

E5   A5   B5   A5
Stacy's mom has got it goin' on.

Verse 1

E5   A5   B5 A5 E5   A5
   Stacy can I come over after scho - o - o - o - ol?

B5   A5
(After school)

E5   A5   B5   A5   E5   A5
   We can hang a - round by the po - o - o - o - o - o - o - ol,

B5   A5
(Hang by the pool).

E5   A5   B5   A5   E5 A5
   Did your mom get back from her business trip,

B5   A5
(Business trip)

E5   A5   B5   A5   E5   A5
   Is she there or is she tryin' to give me the sli - i - i - i - ip?

B5   A5
(Give me the slip)

           G#5   A5
You know I'm not the little boy that I used to be

     G#5   A5
I'm all grown up now baby, can't you see,

Chorus 1

  A5   **E5**   **B5**   **C♯5**
Stacy's mom has got it goin' on
       A5 **E5**   **B5**   **C♯5**
She's all I want and I've wait - ed for so long
A5   **E5**   **C(♭5)**   **C♯5**
Stacy can't you see, you're just not the girl for me
  A5
I know it might be wrong, but
B5   **(E5)**
I'm in love with Stacy's mom.

Link

E5   **A5**   **B5**   **A5**
Stacy's mom has got it goin' on,
E5   **A5**   **B5**   **A5**
Stacy's mom has got it goin' on.

Verse 2

E5   **A5**   **B5**   **A5**   **E5** **A5**
  Stacy do you re - member when I mowed your lawn
B5   **A5**
(Mowed your lawn),
E5   **A5** **B5**   **A5** **E5**   **A5**
  Your mom came out,   with just a towel o - o - o - o - on,
B5   **A5**
(Towel on).
E5   **A5**   **B5**   **A5**   **E5**   **A5**
  I could tell she liked me from the way she stared
     B5   **A5**
(The way she stared)
E5   **A5**   **B5**   **A5**   **E5**   **A5**
  And the way she said,   you missed a spot over the - e - e - e - ere
B5   **A5**
(Spot over there).
     G♯5   **A5**
And I know that you think it's just a fantasy
     G♯5   **A5**
But since your dad walked out, your mom could use a guy like me.

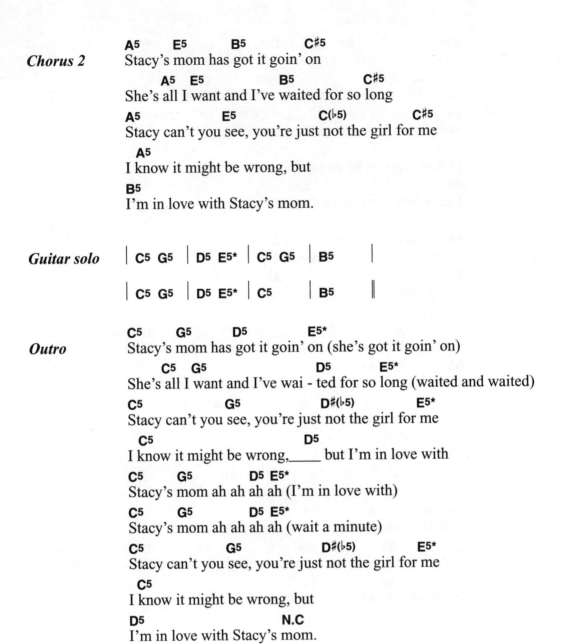

Chorus 2

A5   E5   B5   C#5
Stacy's mom has got it goin' on
        A5 E5   B5   C#5
She's all I want and I've waited for so long
A5   E5   C(b5)   C#5
Stacy can't you see, you're just not the girl for me
   A5
I know it might be wrong, but
B5
I'm in love with Stacy's mom.

Guitar solo | C5 G5 | D5 E5* | C5 G5 | B5 |

                | C5 G5 | D5 E5* | C5 | B5 ||

Outro

C5   G5   D5   E5*
Stacy's mom has got it goin' on (she's got it goin' on)
      C5 G5   D5   E5*
She's all I want and I've wai - ted for so long (waited and waited)
C5   G5   D#(b5)   E5*
Stacy can't you see, you're just not the girl for me
   C5   D5
I know it might be wrong,____ but I'm in love with
C5   G5   D5 E5*
Stacy's mom ah ah ah ah (I'm in love with)
C5   G5   D5 E5*
Stacy's mom ah ah ah ah (wait a minute)
C5   G5   D#(b5)   E5*
Stacy can't you see, you're just not the girl for me
   C5
I know it might be wrong, but
D5   N.C
I'm in love with Stacy's mom.

STOCKHOLM SYNDROME

WORDS & MUSIC BY MATTHEW BELLAMY, CHRIS WOLSTENHOLME & DOMINIC HOWARD

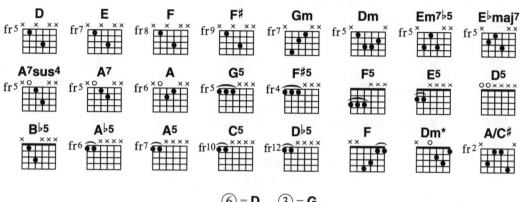

⑥ = D   ③ = G
⑤ = A   ② = B
④ = D   ① = E

Intro   ‖: N.C. | N.C. | N.C. | N.C. :‖

Verse 1

(D)
I won't stand in your way,—

        (E) (F)   **(F♯)**
Let your hat - red grow.—

Gm
And she'll scream,

Dm
And she'll shout,

    Em7♭5   **E♭maj7**
And she'll—— pray,—

    A7sus4   **A7**
And she had—— a name,—

     A
Yeah she had— a name.—

Verse 2

(D)
And I won't hold you back,

　　　　　(E) (F)　　**(F♯)**
Let your an - ger　　rise.—

　　　　Gm
And we'll fly,

　　　　Dm
And we'll fall,

　　　　Em7♭5　　　**E♭maj7**
And we'll—— burn,—

　　　　　　A7sus4　　　**A7**
And no-one will—— recall,—

　　　　A　　　　**G5 F♯**
No-one will— recall.—

Link 1　| **F5** | **F5** | **F5** | **F5** ||

Chorus 1
F　　**A/E**　　**Dm***
This is the last time I a - bandon you,

　　　　　F　**A/C♯**　　　**Dm***　**B♭5**
And this is— the last time I for - get you.—

I wish I could.

Link 1　| **F5 A♭5** | **A5 C5 D♭5** | **N.C.** | **N.C.** ||

Verse 2

(D)
Look to the stars,

　　　　　　(E)　　**(F)**　　　**(F♯)**
Let hope burn in your—— eyes.—

　　　　Gm
And we'll love,

　　　　Dm/F
And we'll hate,

　　　　Em7♭5　　　**E♭maj7**
And we'll—— die,—

　　　A7sus4　　　**A7**
All to no—— avail,—

　　　　A　　　**G5 F♯**
All to no— avail.—

86

Link 2 | F5 | F5 | F5 | F5 ‖

Chorus 2
```
F          A/E         Dm*
```
This is the last time I a - bandon you,
```
          F     A/C♯        Dm*      B♭5
```
And this is— the last time I for - get you.—

I wish I could.

Instr. | F5 A♭5 | A5 C5 D♭5 | N.C. | N.C. | N.C. | N.C. |

| (D) | (D) | (C) | (C) | (D) | (D) |

| (F) | (F) | Gm | Dm | F |

| Em7♭5 | E♭maj7 | A | A | A | N.C. G5 F♯5 ‖

Chorus 3
```
F          A/E         Dm*
```
This is the last time I a - bandon you,
```
          F     A/C♯        Dm*      B♭5
```
And this is— the last time I for - get you.—

I wish I could.

Link 3 | F5 A♭5 | A5 C5 D♭5 | F5 A♭5 ‖

Outro
```
A5        C5    D♭5      (D)
```
  I wish—— I   could.

‖: (D) | (D) | (D) | (D) :‖

| D5 | D5 | D5 | D5 ‖

TAINTED LOVE

WORDS & MUSIC BY ED COBB

G5   B♭5   E♭5   C5

Intro   ‖: E5 | E5 | E5 | E5 :‖

Verse 1

E5
Some - times I feel I've got to run away,

I've got to, get away

From the pain you drive in the heart of me.

The love we share seems to go nowhere,

And I've lost my life,

For I toss and turn, I can't sleep at night.

Chorus 1

E5   G5
   Once I ran to you (I ran)

Now I run from you,
B♭5
   This tainted love you've given,
 C5
I give you all a boy could give you,
                    G5
Take my tears and that's not nearly all,

Tainted love,

Tainted love.

Verse 2

G⁵
Now I know I've got to run away,

I've got to get away,

You don't really want any more from me

To make things right,

You need someone to hold you tight,

And you think love is to pray,

But I'm sorry I don't pray that way.

Chorus 2

E⁵   **G⁵**
  Once I ran to you (I ran)

Now I run from you,
B♭⁵
  This tainted love you've given,
  C⁵
I give you all a boy could give you,
                                   G⁵
Take my tears and that's not nearly all,

Tainted love, tainted love.

| **G⁵** | **G⁵** | **G⁵** | **G⁵** | ‖

Bridge

G5
Don't touch me please,

I cannot stand the way you tease.

I love you though you hurt me so,

Now I'm gonna back my things and go.

Touch me baby, tainted love,

Touch me baby, tainted love,

Chorus 3

E5   G5
  Once I ran to you (I ran)

Now I run from you,
B♭5
  This tainted love you've given,
  C5
I give you all a boy could give you,
                                     G5
Take my tears and that's not nearly all,

Tainted love, tainted love.

Tainted love, tainted love.

TAKE ME OUT

WORDS & MUSIC BY ALEXANDER KAPRANOS & NICHOLAS McCARTHY

Intro | E5 | E5 | E5 | E5 ‖

Verse 1

                Am7   **D**
So if you're lonely
               G **Bm7**   **Em**
You know I'm here waiting for you
            Am7   **D**
I'm just a crosshair
              G   **Bm7**   **Em**
I'm just a shot a - way from you

Verse 2

                Am7   **D**
And if you leave here
              G   **Bm7**   **Em**
You leave me broken, shattered I lie
           Am7   **D**
I'm just a crosshair
              G   **Bm7**   **Em**
I'm just a shot, then we can die.

| G5 A5 | E5 | G5 A5 | E5 ‖

Link

G5   **D5**   **F5**   **C5**   **E5** | E5 | Em* | Em* ‖
I know I won't be leaving here   with you.

Slower tempo
| Em* | Em* | Em* | Em* ‖

| Em7 | Em7 | Am7 | Bm7 |

| Em7 | Em7 | Am7 | Bm7 ‖

Chorus 1

Em⁷
I say don't you know

You say you don't know
Am⁷
I say,
Bm⁷
Take me out!

Chorus 2

Em⁷
I say you don't show

Don't move, time is slow
Am⁷
I say,
Bm⁷
Take me out!

| **Em⁷** | **Em⁷** | **Am⁷** | **Bm⁷** ‖

Chorus 3

Em⁷
I say you don't know

You say you don't know
Am⁷
I say,
Bm⁷
Take me out!

Chorus 4

Em⁷
If I move this could die

If eyes move, this could die
Am⁷
I want you
Bm⁷
To take me out!

| **E⁵** | **E⁵** ‖

Bridge 1

> Am   C6   D6
> I know I won't be leaving here (with you)
>   Am   C6   D6
> Oh, I know I won't be leaving here
> Am   C6   D6
> I know I won't be leaving here (with you)
> Am   C6   D6 Em7 | Em7 | Am7 | Bm7 ‖
> I know I won't be leaving here with you.

Chorus 5

> Em7
> I say don't you know
>
> You say you don't know
> Am7
> I say,
> Bm7
> Take me out!

Chorus 6

> Em7
> If I wane, this could die
>
> If I wait, this could die
> Am7
> I want you
> Bm7
> To take me out!

Chorus 7

> Em7
> If I move this could die
>
> If eyes move, this can die
> Am7
> C'mon,
> Bm7 N.C.
>   Take me out!
>
> | Em* | Em* | Am7 | Bm7 | E5 | E5 ‖

Bridge 2

> Am   C6   D6
> I know I won't be leaving here (with you)
>   Am   C6   D6
> Oh, I know I won't be leaving here
> Am   C6   D6
> I know I won't be leaving here (with you)
> Am   C6   D6 Em* | Em* | Em* | Em* ‖
> I know I won't be leaving here with you.

THIS PICTURE

WORDS & MUSIC BY BRIAN MOLKO, STEFAN OLSDAL & STEVE HEWITT

C   Em   Am   F   E

Capo first fret

Intro | C | C | C | C   ‖

Verse 1

G
  I hold an image of the ashtray girl

Em
  As the cigarette burns on my chest,

C
  I wrote a poem that described her world,

Em
  And put our friendship to the test.

Am
  And late at night whilst on all fours

Em
  She used to watch me kiss the floor.

F
  What's wrong with this picture?

C
  What's wrong with this picture?

Verse 2

                  Em
Farewell the ashtray girl,

             C
Forbidden snowflake.

              Em
Beware this troubled world,

               Am
Watch out for earth - quakes.

           Em
Goodbye to open sores,

           F
To broken sema - phore.

            C
We know we miss her

We miss her picture.

Chorus 1

<pre>
          F   C
          Some times it's faded,

                          F
          Disintegrated,

                          C
          For fear of growing old.
          F   C
          Some times it's faded,

                          F
          Assassinated,

                          C
          For fear of growing old.
</pre>

Verse 3

<pre>
                          Em
          Farewell the ashtray girl

                    C
          Angelic fruitca - ke.

                          Em
          Beware this troubled world

                    Am
          Control your in - take.

                          Em
          Goodbye to open sores

                          F
          Goodbye and further - more

                          C
          We know we miss her,

          We miss her picture.
</pre>

Chorus 2

<pre>
          F   C
          Some times it's faded

                          F
          Disintegrated

                          C
          For fear of growing old.
          F   C
          Sometimes it's faded

                          F
          Assassinated

                          C
          For fear of growing old.
</pre>

Bridge

    E   Am
    Hang on

            E
Though we try

    Am
It's gone.

    E   Am
    Hang on

            E
Though we try

    Am
It's gone.

Chorus 3

    F   C
        Some times it's faded

                  F
Disintegrated

                    C
For fear of growing old.

    F   C
        Some times it's faded

                  F
Assassinated

                    C
For fear of growing old.

Outro

    F   C
    Can't stop growing old.

    F   C
    Can't stop growing old.

    F   C
    Can't stop growing old.

    F   C
    Can't stop growing old.

    F
    Can't stop growing old.

TIME IS RUNNING OUT

WORDS & MUSIC BY MATTHEW BELLAMY, CHRIS WOLSTENHOLME & DOMINIC HOWARD

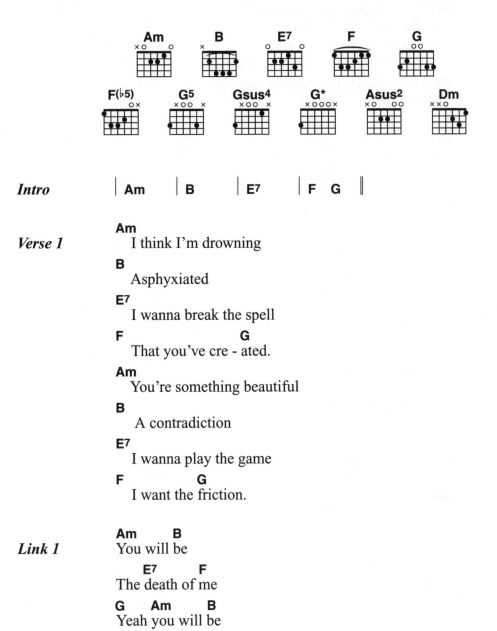

Intro | Am | B | E7 | F G ||

Verse 1

Am
I think I'm drowning

B
Asphyxiated

E7
I wanna break the spell

F   G
That you've cre - ated.

Am
You're something beautiful

B
 A contradiction

E7
I wanna play the game

F   G
I want the friction.

Link 1

Am   B
You will be

    E7   F
The death of me

G   Am   B
Yeah you will be

    E7   F G
The death of me.

Pre-chorus 1

    F(♭5) F
    Bu - ry it

    G5   **Gsus4** **G*** **Asus2 Am**
      I won't let   you bu - ry it

    C   **Cadd9 C Cmaj7 F(♭5)**   **F**
      I   won't let you   smo - ther it

    G5   **Gsus4 G***   **Asus2 Am**
      I won't let   you   mur - der it

Chorus 1

    C   **F**
      Our time is running out

    G   **Am**
      Well our time is running out

    C   **F**
      You can't push it underground

    G   **Am**   **F G**
      You can't stop it screaming out.

Instrumental | **Am** | **B** | **E7** | **F** **G** ‖

Verse 2

    Am
      I wanted freedom

    B
      Bound and restricted

    E7
      I tried to give you up

    F   **G**
      But I'm ad - dicted.

    Am
      Now that you know I'm trapped

    B
      Sense of elation

    E7
      You'd never dream

      F   **G**
    Of breaking this fix - ation

Link 2

    Am   **B**
    You will squeeze

        E7   **F** **G**
    The life out of me.

Pre-chorus 2   As Pre-chorus 1

Chorus 2

   C   F
Our time is running out

   G   Am
Well our time is running out

   C   F
You can't push it underground

   G   Am   C
You can't stop it screaming out.

Bridge 1

                    Dm
How did it come to this?

          Am   Dm
Ooh ooh ooh, yeah, yeah, yeah, yeah, yeah,

          Am   Dm
Ooh ooh ooh, yeah, yeah, yeah, yeah, yeah,

          Am   E7
Ooh ooh ooh, yeah, yeah, yeah, yeah, yeah.

Instrumental 2 | Am | B | E7 | F G |

                    | Am | B | E7 | F G   ‖

Link 3

          Am   B
Yeah you will suck

          E7   F G
The life out of me.

Pre-chorus 3   As Pre-chorus 1

Chorus 3   As Chorus 2

Bridge 2   As Bridge 1

Outro | Am | Am | Am | Am   ‖

TRUE NATURE

WORDS & MUSIC BY PERRY FARRELL, DAVE NAVARRO, CHRIS CHANEY,
STEPHEN PERKINS, MARTYN LENOBLE & BOB EZRIN

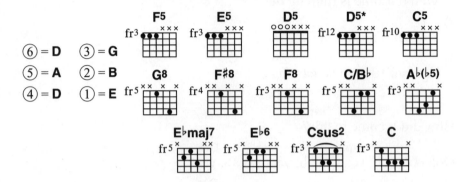

⑥ = D	③ = G
⑤ = A	② = B
④ = D	① = E

Riff
| F5 E5 D5 D5* C5 D5 F5 E5 D5 ‖
Play Riff where indicated in song

Intro
Here we go!   *x4*

Verse 1
D5
Power tripping your luck is switched
　　　　Riff
Oh, so now it's funny
　　　　D5
When it's your turn to laugh
　　　　　　　Riff
You go poke the running joke!

Chorus 1
G8　　　　**F#8**
　Scoring points with God
　　　G8
Get no perfect marks
　　　F#8
But your grades keep falling
G8　　　　**F#8**　　　　　　**F8**
　How you treat the weak is

Your true nature calling.

Link 1   *Riff x4*

D5

Verse 2   Porn chick calls herself a therapist

              Riff

Baby call it what it is,

D5

For all the money in the world

               Riff

We'll go to war for backward heroes.

G8   **F#8**

Chorus 2   Come to rescue you

      F8

Just to lean on you

     F#8

With interests soaring

G8   **F#8**   **F8**

How you treat the weak is

Your true nature calling.

Link 2 | **D5** | **D5** | **D5** | **D5** |

            | **D5** | **D5** | **D5** | **D5**   ‖

Bridge 3 | C/B♭ | A♭(♭5) | E♭maj7 E♭6 | E♭maj7 E♭6 |

| C/B♭ | A♭(♭5) | E♭maj7 E♭6 | Csus2 C ‖

C/B♭   A♭(♭5)
   Please believe

E♭maj7 E♭6   E♭maj7 E♭6
      We live and breathe

C/B♭   A♭(♭5)
    Through native tongue and   poetry

E♭maj7   E♭6   Csus2   C   C/B♭ A♭(♭5)
  All these   years man, we be - lieved,

E♭maj7 E♭6
      Yeah!

Solo   *Riff x4*

   G8   F♯8
Chorus 3   Scoring points with God

     F8
Get no perfect marks

     F♯8
But your grades keep falling

G8   F♯8   F8
   How you treat the weak is

          D5
Your true nature calling.

WARNING SIGN

WORDS & MUSIC BY GUY BERRYMAN, JON BUCKLAND, WILL CHAMPION & CHRIS MARTIN

Dadd9   G   D   A   E   Esus4

F#m   Em/G   E/G#   Gmaj7   F#m7   Em7/A   Dmaj7/F#

Capo first fret

Intro | Dadd9 | Dadd9 | Dadd9 | Dadd9 |

‖: G   D | A   E | G   D | A   E :‖

Verse 1
      G   D
A warning sign,

    A   Esus4 E   G   D
I missed the good part then I realised,

    A   Esus4 E   G   D
I started looking and the bubble burst,

    A   Esus4 E   G   D   A   Esus4
I started looking for excuses.

Verse 2
      G   D
Come on in,

    A   Esus4 E   G   D
I've got to tell you what a state I'm in.

    A   Esus4 E   G   D
I've got to tell you in my loudest tones

    A   Esus4   E   G   D
That I started looking for a warning sign.

| A   Esus4   E | E |

Chorus 1
           D   F#m
When the truth is

      A   E/G#
I miss you.

           D   F#m
Yeah, the truth is

      A   E/G#
That I miss you so.

Guitar solo | G   D | A Esus⁴ E | G   D | A Esus⁴ E |

```
              G         D
Verse 3       A warning sign

              A       Esus⁴        E
                You came back to haunt me

                  G        D
              And I realised,

              A              Esus⁴ E
                That you were an island

                  G           D
              And I passed you by,

              A              Esus⁴ E            G         D
                When you were an island to discover.


              | A        Esus⁴        E     |



              G         D
Verse 4       Come on in,

              A       Esus⁴  E          G          D
                I've got to tell you what a state I'm in.

              A       Esus⁴  E          G       D
                I've got to tell you in my loudest tones

              A       Esus⁴       E        G         D
                That I started looking for a warning sign.


              | A        Esus⁴        E    | E     |



                        D        F♯m
Chorus 2      When the truth is

                      A      E/G♯
              I miss you.

                        D        F♯m
              Yeah, the truth is

                      A           E/G♯
              That I miss you so.

                      Gmaj⁷  F♯m⁷
              And I'm tired,

                              A      E/G♯ | E/G♯       |
              I should not have let you go.
```

Middle　　　　| A　　　　| Em7/A　　| G　　　　| Dmaj7/F♯ |
　　　　　　　Oh.

　　　　　　　| A　　　　| Em7/A　　| G　　　　| Dmaj7/F♯ |

　　　　　　　　　　A　　Em7/A　　　　G　　　　　Dmaj7/F♯
Outro　　　So I crawl back into your open arms.
　　　　　　　　　　A　　Em7/A　　　　G　　　　　Dmaj7/F♯
　　　　　　　Yes I crawl back into your open arms.
　　　　　　　　　　A　　Em7/A　　　　G　　　　　Dmaj7/F♯
　　　　　　　And I crawl back into your open arms.
　　　　　　　　　　A　　Em7/A　　　　　　　　　F♯m
　　　　　　　Yes I crawl back into your open arms.

WASTED TIME

WORDS & MUSIC BY CALEB FOLLOWILL, NATHAN FOLLOWILL & ANGELO PETRAGLIA

E5add#11   E5   G5   D   A

Intro   ‖: E5add#11 | E5add#11 | E5add#11 | E5add#11 :‖

Verse 1

    E5
Oh, it's your life

            G5   E5
Don't you let 'em tell you when to bat your eyes

          G5   E5
You're the only one who's gonna sacrifice

      G5   E5   G5
Makes no difference if you're right or wrong.

  E5
Oh, take that ride

          G5   E5
But I want your little sister by your side

        G5   E5
Maybe a little later we can all collide

     G5   E5   G5
Do our lovin' like a rollin' stone.

Pre-chorus 1

E5add#11
Time on me is wasted time,

Time on me is wasted time,

Time on me is wasted time,

Time on me is wasted.

Chorus 1

```
        D A              D A
          A innocent smile
               D A D A D
        Runnin' free
        E5add#11
        Baby gonna give it like it used to be,

        Baby gonna give it like it used to be.
```

Verse 2

```
        E5
        Show your face
               G5              E5
        Livin' in the shadows like you got no name
               G5         E5
        Enough to make a little girly go insane
               G5        E5         G5
        Be my guest to let it out tonight.
          E5
        But it's ok
               G5            E5
        I know all a - bout the little games you play
               G5       E5
        Shakin' your apple right in my face
                G5              E5              G5
        Only when you know that I'm a beggin' for a bite.
```

Pre-chorus 2   As Pre-chorus 1

Chorus 2   As Chorus 1

Guitar solo

```
| A    | A G | A    | A G | A    | A G | A    | A G ‖

| E5add#11 | E5add#11 | E5add#11 | E5add#11 ‖

| A    | A G | A    | A G | A    | A G | A    | A G ‖

‖: E5add#11 | E5add#11 | E5add#11 | E5add#11 :‖
```

Pre-chorus 3

E5add#11   **(Gbass)**
Time on me is wasted time,

(Ebass)   **(Gbass)**
Time on me is wasted time,

(Ebass)   **(Gbass)**
Time on me is wasted time,

(Ebass)
Time on me is...

        (Gbass)(Ebass)
I'm gon' get yo' Mama

        (Gbass)(Ebass)
I'm gon' get yo' Pa

        (Gbass) (Ebass) (Gbass) (Ebass)
I'm gonna tell everybody just what I   saw.

        (Gbass)   (Ebass)
So won't you show your face (show your face)

        (Gbass)(Ebass)
Your little apple   shaker (show your face)

        (Gbass) (Ebass)
I know the love you gave (show your face)

        (Gbass) (Ebass)   **(Gbass)**
I know the love you take, ah! (show your face).

Chorus 3

D A   D A
     An innocent smile

        D A D A D
Runnin' free

E5add#11
Baby gonna give it like it used to be.

Chorus 4

D A   D A
     An innocent smile

        D A D A D
Runnin' free

E5add#11
Baby gonna give it like it used to be,

Baby gonna give it like it used to be,

Baby gonna give it like it used to be,

Baby gonna give it like it used to be.

WONDERBOY

WORDS & MUSIC BY JACK BLACK & KYLE GASS

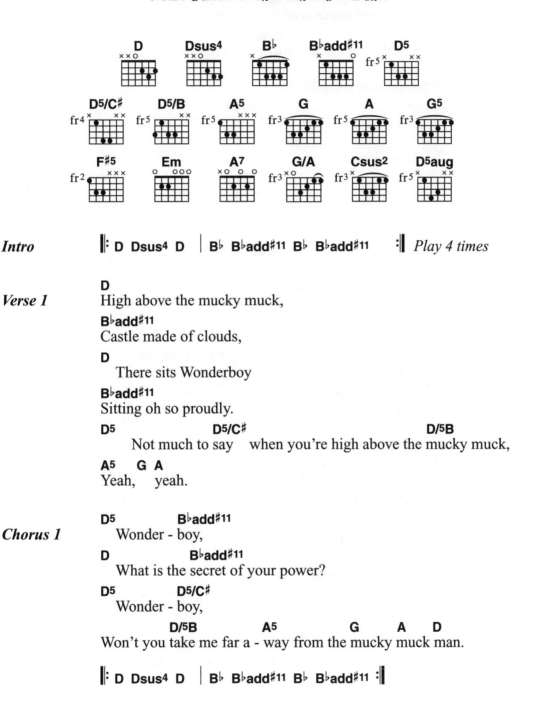

Intro

‖: D Dsus4 D | B♭ B♭add#11 B♭ B♭add#11 :‖ *Play 4 times*

Verse 1

D
High above the mucky muck,

B♭add#11
Castle made of clouds,

D
   There sits Wonderboy

B♭add#11
Sitting oh so proudly.

D5   D5/C#   D/5B
     Not much to say   when you're high above the mucky muck,

A5   G A
Yeah,   yeah.

Chorus 1

D5   B♭add#11
  Wonder - boy,

D   B♭add#11
  What is the secret of your power?

D5   D5/C#
  Wonder - boy,

              D/5B   A5   G   A   D
Won't you take me far a - way from the mucky muck man.

‖: D Dsus4 D | B♭ B♭add#11 B♭ B♭add#11 :‖

Verse 2

D   B♭add#11
Now it's time for me to tell you about young Nasty Man,

                                D
Archrival and nemesis of Wonderboy,

                        B♭add#11
With powers comparable to   Wonderboy.

        D5
What powers you ask?

                                        D5/C#   D/5B
Well how about the power of   flight, that do anything for you?

                                A5
It's levitation , Holmes.

                                        G5   F#5
How about the power to kill a Yak from 200 yards a - way,

        Em
With mind bullets!

A7   G/A
    That's telekinesis Kyle,

                                        A
How about the power   to move you.

Verse 3

D   B♭add#11   D
History of Wonderboy, and young Nastyman,

B♭add#11
        Rigagoo-goo, rigagoo-goo.

        D5
The secret to be told,

    D5/C#
A gold chest to be bold,

        D/5B   A   G A
And blasting forth with three part harmo - ny. Yeow!

Chorus 2

D5   B♭add#11
    Wonder - boy,

D   B♭add#11
    What is the secret of your power?

D5   D5/C#
    Wonder - boy,

                D/5B   A5   G   A   D
Won't you take me far a - way from the mucky muck man.

Verse 4

D   B♭add#11
Well Wonderboy and young Nastyman joined forces

                                                            D
They formed a band the likes of which have never been seen!

                                        B♭add#11
And they called themselves Te - nacious D.

cont.   That's right!

D5   **D5/C♯**
Me and KG, (that's me)

D/5B   **A5**   **G   A**   **Csus2 G D5**
   We're now Ten - a - a - a - a - a - cious D,

Come fly with me, fly!

Solo | **D5** | **D5aug** | **D5** | **D5aug** |

         | **D5** | **D5/C♯** | **D5/B** | **G A**   ‖

         D5   **B♭add♯11**
Chorus 3   Wonder - boy,

         D   **B♭add♯11**
         What is the secret of your power?

         D5   **D5/C♯**
         Wonder - boy,

                D/5B   **A5**   **G**   **A**   **D**
         Won't you take me far a - way from the mucky muck man.

Outro   Oh!

         D5aug   **D5**
         Take my hand, young Nastyman,

         And we'll fly.

                      D5
         Bring out your broad sword,

                   D5aug
         There's the Hydra,

                 D5
         Slice his throat!

                  D5aug
         And grab his scrote.

         You take the high road,

                  D5aug
         I'll take the low.

         D5
         There's the crevasse,

         D5aug   **D5**
         Fill it with your mighty juice.

Relative Tuning

The guitar can be tuned with the aid of pitch pipes or dedicated electronic guitar tuners which are available through your local music dealer. If you do not have a tuning device, you can use relative tuning. Estimate the pitch of the 6th string as near as possible to E or at least a comfortable pitch (not too high, as you might break other strings in tuning up). Then, while checking the various positions on the diagram, place a finger from your left hand on the:

5th fret of the E or 6th string and **tune the open A** (or 5th string) to the note Ⓐ

5th fret of the A or 5th string and **tune the open D** (or 4th string) to the note Ⓓ

5th fret of the D or 4th string and **tune the open G** (or 3rd string) to the note Ⓖ

4th fret of the G or 3rd string and **tune the open B** (or 2nd string) to the note Ⓑ

5th fret of the B or 2nd string and **tune the open E** (or 1st string) to the note Ⓔ

| E or 6th | A or 5th | D or 4th | G or 3rd | B or 2nd | E or 1st | Head |

Nut

1st Fret

2nd Fret

3rd Fret

4th Fret

5th Fret

Reading Chord Boxes

Chord boxes are diagrams of the guitar neck viewed head upwards, face on as illustrated. The top horizontal line is the nut, unless a higher fret number is indicated, the others are the frets.

The vertical lines are the strings, starting from E (or 6th) on the left to E (or 1st) on the right.

The black dots indicate where to place your fingers.

Strings marked with an O are played open, not fretted. Strings marked with an X should not be played.

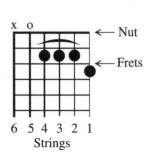

The curved bracket indicates a 'barre' - hold down the strings under the bracket with your first finger, using your other fingers to fret the remaining notes.